Song On A Hill
Traces Of Black and Blue

George W. Ramphrey

Ammadelle
Publishing Company
DALLAS, TEXAS

To Tina

Best Regards,

George W

Ramp

Song On A Hill
Traces Of Black and Blue
All Rights Reserved
Copyright © 2015 George W Ramphrey
Second Printing 2017

Cover Photo © 2015 All rights reserved - used with permission

Ammadelle Publishing Company
Dallas, Texas

ISBN-13: 978-0-9995661-0-7

Printed in the United States of America

DEDICATION

I dedicated this book to the memory of my beloved Mother Neva, my talented brother, Johnny and the amazing Mrs. Susie.

ACKNOWLEDGEMENTS

Thanks to the following contributors for their support and assistance:

My wife offered patience, advice, and encouragement and my son, contributed artistic input.

Dr. Mark Weiss, talented photographer, for the image "A Boy on a Hill."

Dr. Charles Smith, a loyal friend, who gave invaluable encouragement and guidance.

Song On A Hill

INTRODUCTION

Song on a Hill is a poignant story of the trials and tribulations of a boy who grew up in the South in the summer of 1962. Cherished experiences shared by family and friends in Vicksburg, Mississippi. Life was vividly portrayed and came to fruition through breathtaking scenery, Southern customs, and historical depictions. The story was at the hands of an overbearing Stepfather. Agony and pain were evident as the boundaries of the human spirit. What was the destiny of this Southern family? Maybe, the answer was in the wind from a Song on a Hill.

Song On A Hill

Song On A Hill

CHAPTER 1
LEAP OF FAITH

Sunday morning of July 8, 1962, started in a familiar, chaotic way. My mother wandered about at 7:00 am in a frantic state of mind. The alarm clock hadn't sounded. For this reason, the family over-slept. Mother planned a 5:30 am awakening. This problem created a discrepancy of an hour and a half.

Sarah, my sister, invited us to her twenty-first birthday party at 1:00 pm. The dilemma was that we resided in Vicksburg and Sarah lived in Greenville. The trip was a two-hour drive up Highway 61 North. Mother offered Sarah assistance in birthday party preparations by 9:00 am. This arrangement insured an opportunity for church attendance from 11:00-12:00. Also, we had to get dressed.

Mother yelled, "Hey, Ronnie, David Lee, get up the alarm didn't sound. We've overslept, and it's 7:00 am. Do you guys even hear me? Lord of mercy! We're running late, and you need to get out of bed."

"What? Man alive," I said as I wiped my eyes and cleared the cobwebs. I stayed up late to play cards and monopoly with Ronnie. Also, we watched TV until the network ended transmission. Then the TV set was turned off until morning. A sign-off logo of an Indian-head test pattern wasn't entertainment. Sometimes, in our neighborhood, if conditions were right, we received adequate TV reception. We received broadcasts from three television stations. Two of the stations originated out of Jackson, Mississippi. They were WLBT and WJTV. The other station was KNOE that transmitted from Monroe, Louisiana. We received good reception as we rotated the outside antenna. Also, we adjusted rabbit ears located atop our TV set. We twisted and turned

1

control knobs when we became frustrated with a cloudy picture. Over time, this practice resulted in broken and dysfunctional buttons. In this case, we attached a pair of vise grip pliers to the control knobs as a panacea for this technical problem. A backup set of pliers needed to be required by the FCC for all TV sets. We were amused because Mother hid the vise grip pliers when we had visitors.

"I mean it, rise and shine. David Lee quit daydreaming. Y'all are beginning to get on my nerves."

"Mama, can I have five more minutes to rest my eyes?" Ronnie said as he cuddled up in a fetal position under covers. As he hugged his pillow and closed his eyes, he drifted off into dreamland. Ronnie slept more than any human being that I'd ever known. I theorized that he slept for days if no one awakened him. One asked the question after Ronnie's sleep marathons, "What's the date?"

"I'm going to pop the fire out of you boys. I repeat this is the last time that I'm going to tell y'all to get up and get ready. I'm counting to three, and then I'll start swinging my belt." She counted and announced, "Here I come!" Mama approached my bed with her belt.

She jerked the covers off my bed. I scurried my skinny thirteen-year-old body, to the bathroom. The only thing that separated me from the great outdoors was a thin sheet and a pair of oversized boxers. I laughed as I shut the bathroom door. I washed my face and brushed my teeth.

"David Lee, you can bathe later. I forgot that you're not going with us. Let Ronnie bathe first because he's going with me to visit Sarah in Greenville. She has reserved, for her birthday party, the facilities at Strange Park. This party is going to be a big deal. She's expecting about twenty-five or thirty family guests to attend. Are you sure that you don't want to go with us?"

"No Ma'am. Don't you remember? I'm going hiking with Billy and two of his brothers in the Vicksburg National Military Park this morning. We've been planning this trip for over a week. Can Ronnie go hiking with us?"

"No, Ronnie is going with me. He's looking forward to attending Sarah's birthday party. David Lee, make sure that you've finished all your chores before you go gallivanting all over God's Creation."

"Yes Ma'am, I finished all my chores yesterday. I wanted to make sure that nothing was going to prevent me from going on this much-awaited hike."

"Well, make sure that you return home by early afternoon in case Mitch needs your help. He worked the graveyard shift last night and should return home this morning by 9:00 am. Of course, be careful and don't awaken him when you return. We don't need any additional trouble or drama."

"I will Mother. I should return between 1:00 and 2:00 pm and I promise that I'll be extra quiet. I don't want any problems either."

There was a weak knock on the bathroom door followed by a feeble attempt to enter.

"I hear you knocking, but you can't come in." Unfortunately for some, I was a morning person and blessed with an uncanny ability of irritating others who suffered from the morning blahs.

"Mama, David Lee won't let me in the bathroom, and he's going to make us late."

3

"What? Little brother, come on in because the water's fine. Besides, you're turning the doorknob the wrong way. The door isn't even locked."

Ronnie entered the bathroom in a catatonic state. His dishwater blonde hair stuck out like a bad habit. He had a prominent cowlick in his hair. There was a way to control this calamity. Cowlicks had to be plastered down with large quantities of hair oil or pomade.

Ronnie entered. I remarked, "Well, don't you look like the walking dead? Mama, he's picking on me again."

"David Lee, I 'm going to pop your jaws a winding if you bother my baby again. Mother ran and grabbed Ronnie and gave him a big hug. She followed by giving him kisses. She faced me and gave me a bemused gander. Then she messed up my slicked back hair. "Mama, you just wasted a half a bottle of Fitch hair oil."

"You have enough oil on your hair to grease a car," Ronnie remarked. He then pinched and held his nose as a sign of nastiness.

"I'm sorry. Please accept my apology because a jest breaks no bones, my dear brother." Then I struck a pious pose with my left index finger pointed to the ceiling. I resembled an insincere Ichabod Crane as I assumed this comical stance.

Ronnie turned around and punched me in the upper arm and said, "I'm not a jester, but I can 'just' break your bones!" We laughed at the witty comment. He was articulate and intelligent for a ten-year-old.

"Ronnie, hurry up and finish your bath. I'm leaving here in a few minutes with or without you. You'd better get into high gear."

"Ok, Mama, I'm almost ready. Please don't leave me. I'm coming."

"David Lee, you need to be careful on your hiking trip," Mother said. "Also, eat a bowl of cereal and drink a glass of milk before you go," she pleaded. "I worry about your health."

"I'll be alright, Mama. I'm just not hungry right now. I'll make sure that I eat when I return."

"David Lee, you need to eat more because you're nothing, but skin and bones. Sweetheart, you resemble a bean pole. I worry about your health."

"I'll get something to eat when I get hungry, I promise."

Mother's comment struck a sensitive nerve because I received kidding about my slight physique for years. I was the object of ridicule and heard jokes like I had a striped suit with only one stripe. Also, I listened to the joke that I had to run around in the shower to get wet. These jokes were so trite that I became desensitized to these timeworn remarks. Also, Ronnie reminded me of his crowning achievements. He was bestowed special recognition at a Greenville summer recreation park competition several years ago. He won a blue ribbon and trophy for "Mr. Physique". In the same contest, I was the recipient of a consolation runner-up ribbon for "Mr. Brown Eyes".

"Ronnie, are you ready? Are you out of the tub and dressed?"

"Yes, I am. Let's go, Mama. I'm ready to go to Sarah's birthday party!"

"David Lee. Don't worry about it," Ronnie remarked. "I'll eat any extra cake and ice cream that was for you." Ronnie rubbed his stomach and smacked his lips in an avaricious manner.

"You may eat all my cake and ice cream, my dear brother. When you return, you'll receive a dosage of Pepto-Bismol for your upset stomach. Your act of kindness will not go unnoticed. There will be an Ex-Lax chocolate bar provided to you free of charge. Of course, I'll have the bathroom door locked for your inconvenience."

"Mama, David Lee is picking on your favorite son again."

"You boys behave. Quit all that kidding. Someone is going to get angry in a minute."

By this time, Susan awakened, and Mother asked, "What time do you report to work at Rice's Dress Shop?"

"Mother, did you forget? Today is Sunday, and Rice's Dress Shop isn't open. However, I'm going to attend church services at St. Paul's with my friend Jeanette Jones. After church, we're going to dine at the Old Southern Tearoom. Later, we're going to visit her cousin on National Street. I'm going to meet Jeanette at her home on Chambers Street at 9:00 am. I bathed last night, but I'm still going to have to hurry, or I'll be late."

She removed rollers and teased her thick blonde hair and achieved a Jackie Kennedy bouffant do. Susan multi-tasked and applied makeup while she cascaded in Chanel No.5. One of a bevy of enamored boyfriends gave her a bottle of this expensive perfume as a Christmas present. Susan graduated from Leland High School this year at eighteen. Susan lived with us this summer for six weeks and was a brown-eyed beauty who resembled actress Sandra Dee. An immaculate dresser, she kept abreast of the latest trends and styles. She was a tomboy until the age of fourteen. If someone mistreated us; they faced her wrath. Susan had a strong sense of values. There was never a question where she stood on an issue.

"Please let Sarah know that I wish her a happy birthday. Also, tell her that I'm sorry that I didn't get to attend her birthday party. I forgot that when we planned the hike that it was on her birthday."

"I'll tell her what you said."

"What did you get her as a present?"

"I haven't wrapped it yet, so I'll show it to you." She pulled out a beautiful and elegant ladies outfit. It was gold, metallic blouse. It came with a black, long dress with side slits.

"Wow! That looks expensive. It resembles something that Loretta Young might wear. Are you sure that Gene will let her wear that? I've never seen a dress with a split up the side of the leg".

"Keep up with the times," Susan yelled from the bathroom. "That's the latest in sophistication and style. I guarantee you that Jackie Kennedy would wear it," Susan said. "Also, Sarah can wear what she wants to wear. No woman needs a man to tell her what to wear."

"Mama, please deliver Sarah's birthday present and card from me. Also, inform her that I'm sorry that I couldn't attend. By the way, I bought her the cutest yellow blouse. I special ordered it from Rice's Dress Shop. It cost me a pretty penny!"

"OK, Susan, I'll give her your present and card."

"How do I look? Do you boys think that your Mother still has it?"

7

"You look beautiful, Mama! You resemble the movie star, Rita Hayworth. It must be your auburn red hair." Mother was flattered by my comment as she readied for the trip.

I entered the living room and sat down on the couch and scrutinized our modest home. I enjoyed that we lived in Vicksburg and resided at 217 Ridgeway Street. We were situated in a cul-de-sac in a three-bedroom home with a bathroom and den which was enclosed and converted from a carport. The house constructed in 1954, had 1200 square feet. It had a reddish-brown composition shingled roof and lighted brown asbestos siding. We were the second owners of the home and were residents for a year. We added improvements such as a welded link chain mailbox stand, bricked double barbecue pit, dog pen, decorative porch columns, and railings. In our front flower bed, we had four metal posts that were laid and in concrete. There was a decorative chain that fit through a welded notch at the top of each post. Mother planted petunias, zinnias, begonias, and impatiens in her front flower beds. She planted hydrangea bushes and crape myrtle trees around the perimeter of the house. In the front yard, we had oak, pecan, and mimosa trees. We had a peach and two plum trees in the backyard. Mother and Stepfather, Mitch slept in the front bedroom. Susan's bedroom adjoined their bedroom. I shared the back bedroom with Ronnie. The den was a junk room with a freezer and window unit air conditioner. We had a city light pole at the edge of our driveway which was convenient because it provided additional light for us to play at night. Overall, our home, even though not fancy, was comfortable.

I went outside to get fresh air. I stayed out of the way while they dressed. I was going to bid them farewell from the front yard so, I plopped down on the front steps and awaited their departure. Mother organized and embarked within a few minutes. We exchanged goodbyes and Mother's 1959 red *Chevrolet Bel Air* drove away. They waved goodbye and were gone. I wondered if I made the right decision by staying home as opposed to attending Sarah's birthday party. A sense of vulnerability and doubt enveloped me. However, the negative feelings subsided after I realized that I'd planned an exciting journey. Besides, Mother and Ronnie were to return home early evening.

I sat on the front door steps and adjusted my worn high-top sneakers. I wiggled my toes into the extreme depths of the shoe and achieved an optimum level of comfort. The snugness of the tennis shoes gave me athletic empowerment. Furthermore, when I wore tennis shoes with tight shoelaces, I felt like a speed demon. I identified with the great running back Billy Cannon of LSU and Houston Oiler fame.

The Vicksburg Evening Post's Sunday Edition lay on our driveway. I grabbed it and thumbed to the Sports section and checked the score of the New York Yankees game with the Minnesota Twins. They played yesterday, and I was excited about the result. Yes! The Yankees won by a score of 9 to 8. No homers for Mickey Mantle yesterday, but he went I for 2, and Roger Maris went 3 for 5. I was elated that they'd won the game and predicted a return to the World Series this year.

There was something extraordinary about this Sunday morning in our neighborhood. I heard lawn mowers as they hummed and inhaled the smell of cut grass. The air was saturated with the vibrant sounds of children as they laughed and played. In contrast, there were combative sounds of tomcats that screamed and hissed at each other down the street. I bet they fought over the affections of Jezebel who was a neighbor's promiscuous tabby. In our yard, was a fox squirrel that was attacked by a sky-diving mockingbird. The squirrel scampered up to our oak tree and hunkered down in a clump of thick branches and leaves. As I viewed the sights and sounds, I envisioned the day. Usually, I attended Mass at St. Paul's Catholic Church. However, our hike was in the morning hours which eliminated attendance for morning services. We had the option of attendance for afternoon Mass at the Colored church which was St Mary's. If Mother returned from Greenville early enough, I had the additional option of Good Hope Baptist Church. I knew that God cared less where you attended church if you believed and worshipped. In this day and time, you had to be careful because people were critical about religious preferences. Many disapproved of Catholicism because they thought that Pope John XXIII and President John F. Kennedy ran the country. Also, attendance at a Colored church wasn't socially accepted.

As I read the newspaper, I noticed that our mimosa tree had begun a gradual descent from our yard. At this rate, it was destined to become a permanent resident of a down-the-hill neighbor's landscape. It was inevitable that one day our neighbors were recipients of this misshaped intruder. Also, on the south side of the house, the soil eroded away from the foundation, and there was a small portion of the yard that remained. Mother joked that one day we'd awaken on Pemberton Avenue, which was down the hill. Our pecan tree was barren this year. We hoped that it rebounded and produced pecans in the future.

Our home, atop a hill on Ridgeway Street, had scenery to the northwest that was picturesque and beautiful. The distant hills rolled in a regal manner. The hillsides complemented the impressive solemnity and reverence of Cedar Hill Cemetery. The tombstones were in paralleled rows in geometric designs. When gazed at from afar it conjured an image of white and green organizational splendor. In front of the cemetery, was well-traveled Sky Farm Avenue. As you traveled its length, you were next to a spikey, grayish-white, metal fence which bordered the cemetery. Reckless drivers who went astray had damaged the fence. The mishaps had created openings for neighborhood children. They entered and ventured in the cemetery for curiosity, adventure, and intrigue. Also, it provided a shortcut conduit to the Vicksburg National Military Park.

While I anticipated the arrival of Billy and his brothers, I amused myself as I jumped over the front flower bed chain. I began on the bottom step and proceeded toward the top as my attempts were successful. A caveat was that with every jump there was the manifestation of fatigue. In my fantasy world, I visualized myself as the premiere long-jump champion of the US Olympic team. My field event was the final one of the games. A successful leap from the top step secured a Gold Medal for the United States and defeated our perennial nemesis Russia.

I unleashed all the energy and positive thoughts that I had. My body soared high into the air with arms and legs outstretched to their physical limits. As I landed; the heels of my sneakers contacted and glanced off the top of the metal chain. However, I catapulted myself to the winning side of the yard. American fans went crazy and their applause deafened. Since I was a celebrity, I purchased a Hickey Freeman suit and a silk Eton shirt. Of course, this was complemented, with a pair of alligator, saddle wingtip shoes. I appeared fashionable as I waved to adoring fans in my New York City ticker-tape parade. Visions of Nikita Khrushchev as he beat his shoe on a Kremlin table and screamed that he "will bury me" resonated in my head. I participated in these silly competitive games. They occupied a great deal of my time. In the past year, as I experienced humiliation and pain at the hands of my stepfather. These fantasies were a defense mechanism and a form of sublimation.

The reality of the matter was that if I tripped on the chain, then I was a candidate for broken bones, teeth, or fractured pride. Nonetheless, today was for positive thoughts since I fulfilled an Olympic dream. I engineered the leap of the century. Remarkably, I set a "World Record" as I jumped from my front porch step. Thus: USA 117 and Russia 116. Hooray! I was a legend in my mind.

CHAPTER 2
TAKE A HIKE

After twenty-five minutes of strenuous and grueling physical exertions that placed the USA on the Gold Medal stand, I spotted Billy, Joey, and Jimmy. They topped the hill and approached me at a rapid pace. Billy threw the football in quick succession to one brother and then to the other. He threw tight spiral passes with speed and velocity that stung one's hands and body. Yes, Billy was a gifted athlete.

I met Billy when we moved in the neighborhood last year, and we were inseparable. In a family of nine children, Billy had five brothers and three sisters. Billy was a handsome, tanned, athletic young man, dark eyes, and well-groomed black hair. He was thirteen-years-old and played football and baseball. Billy was a loyal and dependable friend. He had a great personality and laughed at my jokes. Also, he was quite the ladies' man. I heard rumors that girls called his home all hours of day and night. He dressed well even though some of his clothes were hand-me-downs. He enunciated every word and had a gift of gab. He was an excellent cook and helped his parents prepare meals.

His brother Jimmy, twelve years of age, was quiet, serious-minded, and shy. He was tall, athletic, brown hair, and brown eyes. When he was excited, he stuttered. He dressed in the same lucky yellow shirt and brown pants with sneakers every day. He carried a football everywhere he went. His favorite subject in school was math and was somewhat of a whiz.

Brother Joey, at eleven years, had a great sense of humor. He had blonde hair, green eyes, short, and stocky and was strong with a muscular build for such a young age. Also, Joey had a speech impediment. He pronounced his

Song On A Hill

R's like W's. Billy said, "Wascally Wabbit" when excited. This statement alerted Joey that he had mispronounced a word. The origination was from a Bugs Bunny cartoon character Elmer Fudd. Therefore, he corrected him respectfully. Joey wore a green baseball cap everywhere he went. He spoke in a loud and boisterous manner and never liked shoes. Often, he took off his shoes and walked barefooted. Joey's favorite subject in school was science. He investigated how things worked with a passion. He was mechanical and asked questions that probed into how machinery operated.

Billy and siblings attended school at St. Francis and St. Aloysius. I was a Catholic, but most of my family was Baptist. However, I attended religious services, for many years, at both Protestant and Catholic churches.

"Good morning, are y'all ready to go?" I asked. "Let's do it," Billy replied in a matter of fact tone.

As I strolled through our neighborhood, my senses reinvigorated with the essence of mowed grass and the smell of honeysuckle. This pleasant combination of smells stimulated my senses and fueled my anticipation for a much-anticipated adventure.

We went down the hill on Pemberton Avenue and crossed Sky Farm Avenue and entered the third gate which was the southeast area of Cedar Hill Cemetery.

After we entered, Billy told Joey, "Stay on the road and no walking or running across the top of the graves."

"Why? Joey responded. Because a ghost might come and get me?"

"No! Because it's disrespectful, don't you know anything?"

Jimmy pointed to a group of graves and asked, "What is the CSA?"

My response was, "That represented the Confederate States of America and their gravesites. There were thousands of Southern soldiers killed at the Battle of Vicksburg. This area of the cemetery was known as 'Soldier's Rest.' That commemorative statue and the headstones honored their sacrifices and legacies."

"What the hell"! Joey blurted out.

Billy said, "Shut up and quit cursing. I need a bar of Lava soap to wash out your nasty mouth."

"Billy, I'm sorry that I cursed. This monument says that 'Old Douglas' was a camel that fought with the Rebels 43rd Regiment. It says that the camel was killed by Yankees and buried here."

"Why did the Yankees kill him?" Jimmy asked.

"I bet they were jealous because they didn't have a camel," Billy replied. "Also, I heard that Confederate President Jefferson Davis wanted to use camels on reconnaissance missions."

Joey said, "I don't know what you're talking about, but I'll take your word for it."

"I figure that when the Yankees killed Old Douglas that the Confederate soldiers ate camel steak," I said.

Jimmy looked perplexed and scratched his head with a confused and inquisitive expression. He asked, "Well, if they ate Old Douglas. Then, what was left?"

"Dem bones, Dem Bones, Dem camel bones." I chanted with glee! Joey and Billy joined in, and we repeated this little ditty about ten times. We wore out the novelty of the moment as we sang this repetitive verse.

We continued and meandered through the cemetery.

I snatched the football from Jimmy and yelled, "Go out for a pass, you guys, and I'll hit you in stride." I hurled the ball and overthrew Jimmy's outstretched arms. The football landed next to a unique and mysterious gravesite.

Jimmy screamed, "Hey, y'all come and come see this. Wow, it's a piano!"

"What?" Billy inquired, "What in the world are you talking about?"

We gathered around the piano tombstone and noticed that there was an attached porcelain picture of a young, beautiful, dark-haired lady. We stood around the grave to study this unique, mysterious phenomenon.

"Do you know what I heard?" Billy asked.

"What you heard about what? Jimmy asked as he scratched the back of his head.

"What do you think? Wake up, Jimmy, what I heard about this piano tombstone." Billy proceeded, "Well, this lady was playing her piano late one night and that her father returned home drunk. Because he was angry at her for being up so late; he beat her to death with her piano stool."

"That's interesting Billy," I replied. "Where did you hear this story?"

"I don't remember. However, I believe it's the truth."

"I'm not saying that you're wrong, but I heard a different story. The story told to me was that this young lady had tuberculosis. Her disease became too severe, and she went to a sanatorium in Arkansas for treatments. Her condition worsened, and she died at a young age."

"Well, the legend is that if you come to the gravesite at midnight and touch the piano keys; that they'll play."

Joey said, "You know I think that I read about this lady's recent death in the Vicksburg Evening Post."

We collapsed on the ground and roared with laughter.

Billy explained, "Joey, the lady died in 1919. That was forty years ago."

We continued down the cemetery road. Joey removed his tennis shoes and tossed them over his shoulder. Then, he ran full speed and caught a football pass from Billy.

Joey said, "Did you see Raymond Berry #82 catch that football?"

Billy replied, "Did you see Johnny Unitas #19 throw the football? That's the question."

We visited an old cave in the back of the cemetery that had a 5' tall entrance and was 12' to 14' in length. Excavated from the side of a hill, we were amazed that it was still in excellent condition. There were signs of previous visitors who trashed the cave with gum wrappers, soda bottles, and Chesterfield, Camel, and Picayune cigarette butts. There were a few, small gray bats attached in clusters inside the dirt pockets at the top of these shallow caves. On the cave floor were disgusting deposits of guano.

On the western edge of the cemetery was a spooky structure that was the Vault. Most people believed that this old building was either a mausoleum or an embalming structure. However, it was the site where bodies stored in a holding vault, in case inclement weather hampered a burial ceremony.

We departed Cedar Hill Cemetery and continued north on Lover's Lane Road. We hiked a mile and reached our ultimate destination which was the Vicksburg National Military Park. We trudged up the steep incline. The roadway was hot with splotches of melted tar. Our bodies baked in the merciless sun. We received temporary relief when occasional fluffy clouds drifted by and blocked the effects of the harsh rays.

We arrived at the top of the hill, and the reward that awaited us was a beautiful view! We saw one of the Observation Towers that was in the Vicksburg National Military Park. They had the appearance of a giant cylinder with a bottom floor and staircase in the middle with four distinct levels that diminished in the area in subsequent elevated levels. Each level had concrete encasements that resembled a cumbersome, but a protective fence. On top of the tower was an American flag that fluttered in the Southern breeze. The tower we observed was the one near Fort Hill.

For fifteen minutes, we raced up and down the tower steps and then headed for Fort Hill. Billy threw the football from the top floor, and we sped down the steps like possessed.

Fort Hill was less than a half mile west of the Observation Tower. Fort Hill was the site of Fort Nogales (means walnut in Spanish). However, Fort Nogales was constructed by the Spanish in the 1790's and abandoned at the beginning of the nineteenth century. Today, there was a hill that had four civil war cannons, deep trenches, and a parking lot for observing the Yazoo Canal (old Mississippi River bed). To the north, we viewed the National Cemetery with 17,000 gravesites of Civil War Union Soldiers. From our lofty and scenic vantage point, the tombstones resembled dominos in a row on a field of green. Also, on the edge of the cemetery, was a gazebo constructed on a distinct small mound that overlooked the gravesites.

Hidden from sight, in a wooded area of the creek, was one of our destinations; the waterfall at Mint Springs. This waterfall, fed by a small stream, flowed over the park road and was a place of distinction in "Ripley's Believe it or Not." It was the only bridge in the world in which the water ran over the bridge instead of under it.

We had followed the park road until Fort Hill. Then we took a precarious route which was considered the unsafe safe way in reaching the bottom of Fort Hill. It was the path less followed. We negotiated the hill at an acute angle and watched where we stepped. On steep sections, we lied down on the hill and grabbed clumps of grass for safety purposes. We moved deliberately onward, and after fifteen or twenty minutes of intrigue and danger, we reached the bottom of the hill. Luckily, a stream was at the foot of the hill! The bottoms of our feet were inflamed, and we took off our shoes and socks and soaked our feet in the clear, cool, creek water. We carried our shoes and put our socks in our pockets. Next, we waded in the creek and threw rocks and stones which made impressive splashes. I picked up an old broken Falstaff beer bottle to throw at a dragonfly, and it flew to a lower bush branch.

I yelled out! "Yikes! Something is on me."

"Is it a snake?" Jimmy asked.

"David, what is on you?" Billy inquired.

I shook like Elvis Presley when he sang, *"All Shook Up."* I had a hungry leech that attached itself to my index finger. It tried to curl around and attach its body to my hand. I flung it. However, it landed on my big toe, and that was when it became interesting! I danced around like a crazed, thirsty Indian who prayed for rain.

Billy and his brothers laughed as they jumped around. They were entertained at my expense as they chanted a chorus of, "Get it off!"

One last fling and I hurled that bloodsucker back to the abyss of the cool water of the creek from whence it came.

We laughed about it, and I learned a valuable lesson in life which was to watch what you grabbed because it might grab you back!

Our next stop was Mint Springs. We were sweaty and musty and did what most southern boys did under similar circumstances. We went skinny dipping! The water refreshed, and the only caveat was to watch where you put your feet. The thought of a hungry snapping turtle submerged in the depths of the water wasn't appealing. We swam and played in the water for ten or fifteen minutes. We had a pleasant time until a water snake swam right between us. Of course, this caused a mass exodus and plenty of shared laughs from all.

We were on our VNMP adventure for three hours and visited one more site before the tour ended. The tallest monument in the Park was the Naval Monument. Admirals Farragut, Porter, Foote, and Davis had statues on the four corners of the monument. Also, they had grates behind the statues that were construction weep holes for the memorial. We noticed that the grill behind Admiral Farragut, which faced south, was removed. Since there was enough room for us to squeeze in, we crawled inside the monument. I was the first daredevil to enter. I was in a prone position and slithered in like a snake. Then, I dropped to the bottom of the monument's dirt floor and was greeted by a musty odor.

"Are you guys coming?"

"I'm sending in my two brothers, and I need for you to help them because they're scared."

"No problem, I'm ready."

I assisted them inside the monument. We were astonished as we looked up at the high ceiling from the inside of the monument. We investigated the dirty interior, and there was trash and an occasional clump of grass that somehow survived. After our eyes adjusted to the darkness, we ran around and screamed for the echo effect.

We waited for tourists to play a trick on them. I memorized a speech that I thought would scare them. "This is Admiral David Farragut, imprisoned in this monument for a hundred years. Please rub my statue's left boot, and my spirit will be released." Then, I remained silent, and they departed with an outlandish story that they'd freed Admiral David Farragut. It was a perfect plan if someone was committed to Whitfield State Mental Institution located near Jackson.

Jimmy asked, "What if they tell the Park Ranger that a bunch of boys trespassed in the Naval Monument?"

"Well, since you put it that way, I suggest that we get the heck out of here. I hate to admit it, but entering this damp and musty place was a bad idea." Then, I contemplated the worst scenario. What if we were trapped? Claustrophobic thoughts dominated my psyche. Jimmy then had an anxiety attack and clutched his chest and had trouble breathing.

Joey had tears in his eyes. Our thoughts were of four Southern boys forever entombed in the largest Union monument in the Vicksburg National Military Park. The inhumanity of it all, this was serious business. If trapped, how were the Park Rangers going to get us out?

We planned for Joey to exit the monument first, followed by Jimmy, Billy, and then myself. We hoisted Joey up to the opening, and he wiggled out. We heard Joey as he screamed from the outside, "I'm alive."

Jimmy followed suit without a problem and prospects of us getting out of this potential mausoleum improved.

Billy said, "Lift me to the opening so that I can exit and then I'll slide back in head first and assist you in getting out."

"That sounds like a good idea," I replied.

I cradled my hands together and made a lift chair for Billy's foot. He put his hand on my shoulder and pushed with a quick thrust and was hoisted high enough and entered the opening and crawled out. Billy, true to his word, squirmed back in and assisted me. I ran and grabbed Billy's hands, and he slid backward. I positioned my head and shoulders in the opening. After we squeezed, strained, and maneuvered on an inch by inch basis, we reached the "Promised Land." We exited the VNMP convinced of our good luck. God had looked after us.

We returned from our ordeal at about 1:00 pm. Mrs. Nancy Jo, the boy's mother, prepared spaghetti with garlic bread. Their household operated on a first come and first serve basis and meals were consumed speedily in a large family. We took our plates of food on the patio and sat around the picnic table.

Billy shadowboxed with his mother, and she said, "Bring it on buddy, but don't hit me in the stomach, because you know, that I'm six months pregnant. However, I can still take you. Put up your dukes."

"Beat him up," Joey yelled.

Mrs. Nancy Jo was a special person who had an excellent relationship with her children. From the outset of marriage, she was to have thirteen children. Thus far, there were nine children and at least one on the way! I think from these calculations that it was safe to predict that one day her goal was met.

I observed their family under the green fiberglass patio covering and was impressed with the mutual love and respect they shared. I envied their closeness and mutual affection. There was something special about this moment as our tan bodies glistened under the shaded patio's green illumination. This effect created an aura of mystique and surrealism. I felt blessed that I had great friends.

Mrs. Nancy Jo sat down next to me and said, "I have something interesting to tell you."

"What is that, Mrs. Nancy Jo?"

"Every evening I come out on the patio to relax and unwind from a busy day. Often, I hear your brother Ronnie on top of the hill singing. He appears to be alone and in his little world. Sometimes he stands, and other times he sits down and sings. However, he has sung for as long as thirty minutes. Have you ever heard him sing?"

"Not that I can remember."

"He's a good singer. I wait in anticipation every night to hear his soothing and soulful voice. That young man has talent. Don't tell him what I said because it might embarrass him or make him feel self-conscious."

"I won't mention it to him. Your secret is safe with me."

"He always positions himself next to a spooky looking tree. Strange as it sounds that tree seems to comfort him."

"Yes, ma'am. Our large pecan tree does appear rather scary at times, but we love that old tree."

"Well, I had better go now, thanks for the delicious spaghetti and Kool-Aid."

"Take care of your little brother, and I'll see you later."

"Good Bye."

I opened their gate and headed for home. I looked up the hill and visualized the location in which Ronnie sang. There it was a spot on the hill in front of our house. There was a clear view to Mrs. Nancy Jo's backyard. I knew that this was the site. Yes, that was it, because it was next to the old pecan tree.

I had ambivalent feelings from Mrs. Nancy Jo's revelations about Ronnie's nightly concerts. I was proud that my brother was a talented singer. However, I had serious concerns that the sadness in his voice was the result of feelings of isolation and loneliness. What was the root of his unhappiness? I had to keep a watchful eye on my brother. I was my brother's keeper.

CHAPTER 3
HEAVEN TO HELL

After I departed Billy's home, I darted up the hill toward my house. Mitch's Jeep parked out front transitioned my mood from one of positivism to one of apprehension. I was hopeful that Mitch was asleep from working the graveyard shift. If he slept a few more hours, I enjoyed additional free time without aggravation. I removed my tennis shoes and entered through the front door. Immediately, I sensed someone in the living room.

"Where in the hell have you been?" Mitch yelled out in a bellowing voice.

I was startled and taken aback. I replied, "I've been down at Billy's house. We went on a hike. Mama knows about it, and she permitted me to go."

Mitch snidely remarked. "Your mother allows you to get away with too damn much. I'm going to Howard's Country Store and pick up a few items, and you're going with me. Go and get your skinny ass in the Jeep," he ordered. "You damn lazy ass boys need to be introduced to work. I'm going to be the one to introduce it to you. Go on and wait for me."

I climbed into the Jeep and noticed a strong smell of whiskey and cigar smoke. I saw a bottle of Jim Beam that protruded out from the driver's seat. Another whiskey bottle was positioned partially on the floorboard. I determined that Mitch had smoked a cigar and took a few healthy swigs of whiskey on his way home from work. He was an employee of the Illinois Central Railroad and worked as a switchman. Hopefully, he refrained from drinking while he drove or worked and didn't endanger lives.

Mitch lumbered out of the house and approached the Jeep in an agitated manner in his 6'2" two-hundred and forty-pound frame. He had an imposing and intimidating figure. Mitch had a large square head, ruddy complexion, and baby face features. His blue eyes pierced and penetrated and had auburn, wavy hair. Ironically, he resembled a giant size caricature of Audie Murphy who was one of my heroes and role models. However, that was where the comparison ended. Audie Murphy was a Medal of Honor recipients and movie star. Mitch was a mean and abusive alcoholic. Because I wanted an amicable relationship, I strove to please Mitch. I completed my chores and tried to be friendly. He said he didn't want to be friends and that children were seen and not heard. My survival depended on me keeping my mouth shut and staying out of harm's way.

Mitch jumped into the Jeep, revved the engine several times, and proceeded down the hill. He lit a cigar, rolled up his denim work shirt sleeves, peered at me with a cold stare, and grimaced. He shifted the gears methodically as we drove thru the neighborhood. We coasted down the hills, and the muffler and tailpipe emitted bellowing sound.

After a few minutes of his contrived cat and mouse game, he said, "Hey, your Aunt Adelle is arriving from New York in the morning, so you had better make sure that you behave. On the dining room table, I left you a list of things that I want you to do this week. If you don't finish them, it is going to be your ass. Do you understand?"

"Yes! I hear you loud and clear."

"Make sure that you understand. Always do what I tell you. I don't want any excuses."

As we traveled down Sky Farm Avenue, I glanced at Cedar Hill Cemetery and recalled that a few hours earlier my life was total bliss. Presently, I felt isolated and emotionally depleted from being bullied and intimidated. I never told my friends of the family problems that I experienced. I feared that they wouldn't associate with someone from an unhappy family. I was embarrassed and figured that they wouldn't understand my situation since they had happy and well-balanced lives. Evidently, my mother loved Mitch and intended to change him. It was a dangerous situation for me. I prayed to God every night for help and guidance.

Heat and smoke rose off the hood of the Jeep as we drove up and down the hills in Vicksburg. The vibration of the motor and the loudness of the muffler stimulated my thought processes and transferred me to another time and place. I thought about how dramatically our lives changed since Mother and Mitch became a couple. Also, I thought about how they met on that fateful day in the summer of 1961 at Long Lake. The lake was twenty miles northwest of Vicksburg. We had a summer lodge that Mother purchased after she and my father divorced in 1960. Mitch was our neighbor who had cookouts and invited us to dine. Mitch was thirty-two years of age and was five years younger than Mother. He was an excellent cook and possessed a certain amount of charm. He was at times the life of the party and was a great conversationalist. Mother was a successful businesswoman and was a good catch with her beautiful red hair, porcelain skin, and nice figure. During this time, Mitch was a continuous source of emotional support to my mother. After six months of courtship, they married. We sold our summer home and life as we knew it changed drastically.

Before they married, Ronnie and I fished, canoed, and went on boat rides. It was a relaxed, stress-free, charmed life that was a pure adventure for young boys. I fished and caught bream, white perch, and an occasional largemouth bass. On the lake, there were branches and logs overloaded with turtles and

28

snakes that basked in the sun. Our lake house was atop stilts and evenings were spent playing outside underneath floodlights. Of course, the night lights attracted swarms of mosquitoes, moths, and a variety of different types of bugs. We played on the platform under our house and viewed scores of hungry garfish. Many were alligator garfish and were six or seven feet in length. We skewered them with frog gigs and sharp sticks, but usually with little success.

One of my favorite past times was when I batted rocks with sticks or boards. Sometimes I employed my black, Louisville Slugger bat that was autographed by Mickey Mantle. We had a long driveway enclosed by a cyclone fence with little traffic. Of course, a homer was when I hit the rock over our front fence. I just made judgment calls on singles, doubles, and triples and this depended on their distance. A missed rock or a foul tip was an out. I played the game in nine innings with three outs allowed every half inning. Since I was a switch hitter, I alternated by batting left-handed for the visitors and right-handed for the home team. I announced the game in the style of Dizzy Dean and Pee Wee Reese. A typical game lasted for about an hour. Those carefree days seemed like ages ago.

"Hey! Are you awake? We're here. Quit that damn daydreaming. Pay attention and gas up my Jeep while I'm in the store. Don't top it off, just put in two dollars."

While I pumped gas, Mitch and the store owner walked outside and stood on the opposite side of the Jeep. Mitch had a fistful of King Edward cigars in his left hand. He carried several cans of Vienna sausage and potted meat. Also, he had a single pack of saltine crackers in a brown paper bag tucked under his right arm.

"Wash that windshield and check the air pressure in my tires."

I heard Mitch, and the store owner as they spoke and their conversation was not to my liking.

The store owner remarked, "Mitch, you've got yourself a sweet deal when you married Mrs. Evelyn. She's got money and good looks." He continued, "Her daughter's attractive too."

"I don't know about all of that. I guess that financially we're making it alright, but it's the damn bratty kids who piss me off. There are going to be some changes made at our house. It's going to be my way or the highway."

I was in shock and couldn't believe my ears. Mitch disrespected my family and me in front of this store owner. The hateful things he said about us were hurtful.

Unfortunately, because of the time exhausted on this outing, it was impossible to attend Mass with Billy. I arrived home and completed my chores. Afterwards, I went to my bedroom and read the comic section of a Grit newspaper. Mother and Ronnie returned at 6:00 pm and Susan returned shortly after that. I thought about Aunt Adelle and her twins and mentally prepared for their visit in the morning. My hopes and expectations were that this Northern invasion of Vicksburg was better than the previous one!

CHAPTER 4
YANKS ARE COMING

I woke up Monday morning and anticipated my Aunt Adelle and children's visit from upstate New York. I hadn't seen my aunt and cousins since we visited their home in New York in 1959. She was my mother's older sister and was thin and attractive. She had a dark complexion, dark eyes, and thick, black, curly hair. She was serious-minded and articulate. She was an avid reader and had an obsession for Mississippi novelist William Faulkner.

Her husband Peter was a big, jovial, hairy Czech whose family resided in Connecticut and New York for two generations. They operated a restaurant in Croton Falls, New York, called the 1869 House. Aunt Adelle referred to her husband as "Big Petah" and her five-year-old twin son as "Little Petah." Of course, every time that she mentioned them in this manner, we reacted with boisterous laughter. She was born and raised in the South but developed a Yankee accent. Mother and her sisters Patsy, Elizabeth, and Marilyn were jealous of Adelle's curls. On their father's farm, as young girls, they saw a cow as it licked its coat. The result was that the hair on the cow curled. For this reason, they had expectations that if the family cow licked their straight hair, their hair would curl. Of course, the outcome was that the cow left a head full of slobber and cud. Mother's stories entertained and were hilarious.

Because of the Civil Rights Movement, political unrest, and riots in Mississippi, Aunt Adelle worried as she traveled to the South. She drove a black, 1961 *Cadillac Fleetwood* with New York License plate that read, "New York, The Empire State." Mother knew that her paranoia kept her sister up countless hours because she feared the Ku Klux Klan.

Song On A Hill

It was 9:00 am on Monday morning when Mother yelled out, "David Lee and Ronnie, your Aunt Adelle just drove up. You boys come and help carry her suitcases."

"Welcome to Mississippi!" Ronnie announced.

Peter and Phyllis, fraternal twins, had awakened from naps. Both had horrid and shocked looks on their faces. Their glassy-eyed stares were reminiscent of children contacted by aliens who spoke with weird accents. The twins were cute and had blonde hair and blue eyes. At five years of age, they were on the chubby side and needed to lose baby fat. The twins were loquacious and finished each other's sentences. They were hilarious, and their northern accents sounded like a foreign language to our Southern ears.

"Sister Adelle, did y'all have an enjoyable trip?"

"No, Evelyn, I was scared to death that we'd be stopped and jailed. Every time that I saw a highway patrolman, I thought that he was going to notice my New York license plates and stop and detain me."

"Well, come on into the house and get a cup of coffee. David Lee and Ronnie will finish unloading your car."

As the day dragged on, we played outside with our cousins and neighbors. After a short time, they relaxed and discovered that the visit wasn't as bad as envisioned. As nighttime approached, we were welcomed by a splattering of rain. Wet and hungry bodies raced into the house and received comfort and refuge.

"Look I have something for you to eat," Mother said as she served us hot bowls of stew, buttered cornbread, and sweet tea.

32

"What is cornbread?" Phyllis inquired.

"Cornbread is tasty, Aunt Adelle replied. "Try it, sweetie."

Phyllis's lack of knowledge of cornbread, which was a staple and Southern delicacy, reminded me of the profound cultural differences between the North and the South. In fact, when we visited New York in 1959, they had no concept of grits, biscuits, buttermilk, or cornbread. After two or three days in upstate New York, Susan cooked supper one evening, but we wanted biscuits and gravy with the meal. Susan drove to a local grocery store and searched for the ingredients. Finally, Susan asked the grocer, "Sir, where is your Martha White self-rising flour?"

"I'm sorry, what did you say?" He asked as if his ears had forsaken him.

Susan reiterated, "Martha White self-rising flour, do y'all carry that brand?"

He stared at us for a moment and then looked in disbelief at us to achieve a better understanding of what she asked. Suddenly, he threw his head back, lifted his arms up over his head, looked up at the heavens, and roared with laughter! We looked at each other perplexed as to why this man was so amused.

The grocer asked, "Are you all Southerners going to fix you all some biscuits?"

"Indeed, we are," Susan stated. "But only if we can find all the necessary ingredients."

"You're in the North, not the South. There's not a market for biscuits up here," he remarked.

Northerners missed out on so much. First, they talked funny, and now I discovered that they don't eat correctly. The North was a desirable place to visit, but I'd never move there.

The sleeping arrangement the duration of their stay was Peter and Ronnie slept in my bedroom. Susan let Aunt Adelle sleep in her room, and she slept on a rollaway bed in the den. I slept on the couch in the living room, and Mitch and Mother slept in their bedroom. There was one bathroom, so this was a challenge and inconvenience since there were eight people.

Susan worked late at Rice's Dress Shop and returned home at seven o'clock. Her perfume was potent and overpowered as it lingered in the doorway and hallway. She greeted everyone and told us that in a few days that she'd planned a tour for Aunt Adelle and children. She stretched her arms over her head, yawned, and excused herself, and went to bed. Strangely, even though it was early evening, we all went to bed. In my case, it was a combination of the satisfying meal and the rhythm of the rain as it tapped on our picture window and created a mood of drowsy contentment. I threw the sheet over my chest and positioned my pillow on the couch. I noticed that our pictures of "Pinkie and Blue Boy" hung crookedly on the wall. I got up from the couch and straightened them and saw that the rain had picked up in velocity. There was a chill in the air, so I jumped back on the sofa. I knocked over Mother's prized ceramic panther. Thank God that it was undamaged because Mother would be heartbroken and I'd be in big trouble. As the sound of the wind and rain became intense, I drifted off into a deep slumber and slept like a newborn baby.

After a few days, the Northern and Southern contentions acclimated to each other's personalities. However, there were distinct cultural differences.

For example, one morning my Aunt Adelle took a bath and yelled out for something. I had a problem understanding what she said.

She yelled, "A tool, I need a tool!"

I was baffled as to what she wanted. I knocked on the bathroom door and asked, "What is it exactly that you want? What kind of tool?"

"No! David Lee. I need a tool because I have shampoo in my eyes!"

"Oh! It's a towel that you want!" I said. "Please, look in the cabinet under the sink, and you'll find a towel," I suggested.

I was quite amused that we still had problems communicating!

Another humorous story that summer involved the twins. One morning as they bathed, Phyllis yelled and cried out. Aunt Adelle and Mother ran into the bathroom and thought that she was injured. As the twins faced each other, Phyllis pointed at Peter's private area.

"What's wrong?" Aunt Adelle asked.

Phyllis cried out! "Peter is my twin, and he has a dinky wink, and I don't have one."

Mother and Aunt Adelle mouths fell open, and they were at a loss for words.

Peter replied, "Phyllis, please don't cry because I'm going to buy you a dinky wink when Susan takes us to town."

After we heard what had transpired in the bathroom, we howled with laughter. Not only was it funny, but it was endearing because the twin brother was chivalrous and wanted to please his sister.

Susan, as promised, took off work for our tour. Our itinerary included the Old Court House Museum, antebellum mansions, and a tour the Vicksburg National Military Park. Susan drove her green 1954 *Desoto*, and we were like sardines in a can. The entourage consisted of Susan, Aunt Adelle, Peter, Phyllis, and me. Ronnie wasn't there because he accompanied Mother on a downtown shopping spree. I rode up front, and Aunt Adelle sat in the back seat with the twins.

Vicksburg was an outstanding city with beautiful trees, flowers, rolling hills, and stately mansions. Aunt Adelle was amazed by the majestic mansion known as "Anchuca." The mansion, built circa 1830, was located, in the vicinity of Cherry and First East Streets. Anchuca was a Choctaw Indian word. It meant "Happy Home" and the brother of Confederate President Jefferson Davis owned the home at one time. President Davis often gave speeches from the balcony of the home. We stopped in front of this beautiful mansion, as the owner stood in the front yard. Susan, a dare-devil, ran out and explained to him that her aunt from New York wanted to tour this beautiful home. The owner agreed and gave us a tour, but it was done fast because he had prior commitments. The exterior of the home was Greek Revival Architecture with massive columns, balcony, and large windows. The oak trees were magnificent. We toured inside the home and found it breathtakingly beautiful. There was an impressive winding staircase and spacious hallway. The parlor décor was exquisite with vases, paintings, an assortment of wall tapestries, and antique furniture. Also, the bedrooms had lavish furnishings, paintings, and canopied beds. Of course, the owner renovated the kitchen and bathroom with modern conveniences. We thanked the gentleman, and Aunt Adelle was ecstatic that she had toured the beautiful and stately "Anchuca." She told us that it reminded her of a mansion in Faulkner's novel *"Sartoris."* We drove by Cedar Grove Mansion on Oak Street, and Aunt Adelle was impressed at this regal structure. We all agreed that Cedar Grove Mansion reminded us of "Tara" from the movie and book *"Gone with the Wind."* Next, we drove to other beautiful antebellum homes in the Cherry Street and Drummond Street area. The homes were magnificent and historically significant.

The next stop on our tour was the Old Court House Museum. This historic building was more than a hundred years old. Built on top of a hill, General Grant and his Union Forces viewed the clock tower during the Battle of Vicksburg in 1863. Today, it was a museum, but in previous times it served as a courtroom for trials and legal matters. We paid our admission and toured the exhibits and artifacts of the Civil War. There was a cultural display that honored the Mississippi Choctaw Indians and their subsequent removal to Oklahoma on the "Trail of Tears." The twins were bored after ten minutes, and the only thing that appealed to them was the gift shop. We bought them both "Johnny Rebel Confederate Caps" and "Confederate Rebel Flags." As we departed the Old Court House Museum, we saw beautiful oak, magnolia, gingko, and crape myrtle trees. The gardenia, azalea, hibiscus, and hydrangea shrubs and bushes were incomparable. Also, there was an assortment of beautiful plants and flowers that spanned the colors of the spectrum of the rainbow. The plants, flowers, and trees thrived on well- manicured and well-maintained grounds.

We saved the best part of the tour for last. It was the Vicksburg National Military Park. The VNMP was sixteen miles of winding turns, rolling hills, deep valleys, and hollows. We had two hours in which to tour this beautiful and significant historical military park. Susan turned on her radio as we headed for Fort Hill. *"Sukiyaki"* played and even though I loved the song, I was clueless as to the Japanese lyrics. We stopped at Fort Hill, and the twins played on the cannons and ran in the trenches. There was a young couple with children who flew kites on the top of Fort Hill. We watched a red and yellow kite as it danced across the light blue sky and performed sophisticated maneuvers. Our next stop was the observation tower that was in close vicinity of Fort Hill. Aunt Adelle forbade her children to climb the precarious tower stairs. I agreed with her and didn't blame her caution. Since they were young, this was traumatic and harrowing. We drove to the Illinois Monument, and the twins were delighted at the hole in the roof. Peter and Phyllis loved the echo effect. They and countless other young tourists yelled until they were hoarse. On the inside walls were plaques that contained a roster of the Union soldiers from Illinois who fought in the Battle of Vicksburg. I had them count the number of steps as we departed from the Illinois Monument. Aunt Adelle helped the twins in this endeavor, and they counted forty-seven steps. I told them they were correct and that this was significant because that represented the number of days in the Siege of Vicksburg. I participated in many field trips to the VNMP and remembered key facts that teachers had taught me about my beloved city. After we drove by the Wisconsin, Alabama, Iowa, Louisiana, New York, Pennsylvania, Mississippi, and Minnesota monuments the tour officially ended.

As we departed the VNMP, Shelley Fabares sang *"Johnny Angel, "* and the twins and Aunt Adelle fell asleep in the backseat. The park filled with tourists and locals in a variety of cars, trucks, buses, motorcycles, and bicycles. There were a few groups who hiked and enjoyed this gorgeous day. We laughed as a 1961 *Chevrolet Impala* and a 1960 *Ford Thunderbird* raced past at high speeds. They passed us if we stood still. I enjoyed outings with Susan in that she was loads of fun and rarely disappointed.

Early in the morning, Aunt Adelle and the twins returned home. It was a great visit, and I was hopeful that we'd see them soon. I was thankful that Mitch stayed out of the picture. I assumed that he frequented the local bars, on

Mulberry Street and Highway 80, during their visit. Nevertheless, it was great that we had a brief reprieve and was thankful that we spent quality time with our relatives. Aunt Adelle invited us to visit her family in two years. She told us that New York City was the sponsor of the World's Fair in 1964. Also, there was a new baseball stadium planned for construction for a new National League team, the New York Mets. Maybe, this time when we visited, a Yankees game was in the plans. Mother and Aunt Adelle discussed the possibility of a boat cruise around the East and Hudson Rivers as it navigated around New York City. The cruise had an itinerary that included, Yankee Stadium, Columbia University, Grant's Tomb, the Statue of Liberty, and the George Washington Bridge. As I heard Mother and Aunt Adelle's discussion about the sights and sounds of New York City, my senses overloaded with the prospect of attendance at the New York World's Fair. I went to bed that night and visions danced in my head of The World's Fair, Empire State Building, the Statue of Liberty, and Yankee Stadium. I dreamt that I caught a baseball hit by Mickey Mantle at Yankee Stadium. Of course, the vision included autographs from Mickey Mantle, Roger Maris, Whitey Ford, and Yogi Berra. Batter up! Play ball!

CHAPTER 5
SOMETHING IN THE AIR

The next morning came fast, and I woke from my sweet dreams abruptly.

"Get up boy! Mitch barked. We're going to Eagle Lake to clean up the deer camp."

"Hurry up. We're leaving in ten minutes."

I dressed in the bathroom and later helped Mitch. We gathered cleaning supplies, rifles, shotguns, ammunition and an assortment of sundries. After a few minutes, we departed. Even though it was twenty-five miles to the deer camp, it took us an hour to drive to the locale. The camp was, situated in a thickly forested area, was near Steele and Black Bayou. We headed north down Highway 61 to Redwood and crossed the bridge. Then, we turned left on Eagle Lake Road and took several gravel and dirt roads that resembled pig trails to reach our destination.

On our journey, Mitch was sullen and preoccupied as he puffed on a cigar and didn't utter a word. The smoke had a strong, and the air had an intoxicating odor. The road filled with fisherman with boats and trailers of every make, style, and size. Also, there were skiers with roundabout sports boats. We observed roadkill which was a combination of stray dogs, raccoons, and an occasional rabbit. I gazed off the main road and noticed that recent rains had created pools of water between the woods and the shoulder of the road. Impressive oak trees were abundant draped in Spanish moss.

The deer camp was an old railroad car mounted on a trailer frame. It was in the corner of gnarly bushes. The structure faced west and had a lone door that served both as an entrance and exit. A combination of Mississippi hardwoods and softwoods shaded the area. There was a gravel driveway in front and directly to the left was a bayou, with an abundance of cypress trees and stumps. The bayou was home to a variety of birds, snakes, turtles, gators, frogs, and fish. Some frequent visitors were raccoons, deer, squirrel, wild pigs, and an occasional black bear. Several years ago it was reported that a panther was spotted as it prowled the banks of the bayou

Deer camp members Rusty, Matt, Alfred, and Charley, were at the camp when we arrived. We removed everything from the structure and placed the contents outside. We swept and mopped the floors, washed dishes, sprayed for bugs, and scrubbed the walls. Also, we cleaned up around the perimeter and picked up trash and burned debris in rusty barrels. It was a hot and tedious job, but vastly improved the appearance of the camp. Charley, who was fourteen and the son of one of the hunters assisted me.

We worked all morning and stopped at noon and ate bologna and cheese sandwiches. However, we had other work assignments that needed our attention. For this reason, we worked late into the night and had to spend the night at the camp.

Mitch said, "If we are going to stay tonight, then we need to know what we're going to eat tonight and in the morning."

Rusty added, "I have a package of deer meat and a couple of sacks of potatoes and onions, however, for breakfast, we're going to need milk, eggs, bacon, and bread."

"OK! I'll drive up to the Lo Sto at Eagle Lake and get those items," Mitch replied.

41

I loved the name Lo Sto. I figured that it was called the Low Store, but with a Southern, colloquial, dialect over time it became a corrupted pronunciation. This well-known store was on the shore of Eagle Lake and sold bare necessities. There was nothing fancy about the Lo Sto, but it had character and charm.

The Jeep's motor sounded louder than usual as we traversed the muddy roads on our way to the store. Mitch swerved and dodged ruts and mud holes in the road that presented potential problems. If we bogged down in the mud, we'd face hours of frustration and isolation. Mitch avoided this issue by leaving the road and driving onto the edges for traction when the road resembled a muddy pond.

The Jeep negotiated these adverse conditions admirably. Suddenly, Mitch pulled the Jeep over to the side of the road and yelled, "Good God! Look at the size of that rabbit."

"I've never seen one that big."

Even though it was summer time and not rabbit season, I wanted to shoot this big rabbit! I grabbed my twenty-gauge shotgun and jumped out of the Jeep. I jumped atop a nearby pile of dead branches and shook them with my foot and yelled, "Hey, get out of there."

Mitch got out of the Jeep in a confused and agitated state and said, "What in the hell do you think that you're doing?"

"I'm going to shoot this big rabbit you're talking about," I explained.

"Boy, you are one dumb ass! I bet that you couldn't empty piss out of a boot if the directions were on the heel. I didn't say 'rabbit,' I said 'rattler,' and that son of a bitch is bigger than my arm and looks to be 7or 8 feet long."

My knees weakened from this unpleasant information, and I backed out of the middle of the wood pile. I took a deep breath, put my shotgun in the back of the Jeep, and jumped into the front seat. My hands shook, and my knees had the consistency of Jell-O. I awaited the upcoming diatribe.

"You're a crazy little bastard! I can't believe that you jumped in a woodpile with the biggest rattlesnake that I'd ever seen. I wish that it would've bitten your skinny ass. Honestly. I don't understand you."

I sat there stoically, with the knowledge that I hadn't heard him correctly because of the noisy Jeep. I wasted my breath if I offered explanations as to what happened. He wasn't in the mood for what he called excuses. Also, he deemed an excuse as a personal affront, and a sign of disrespect. Besides, what he said in anger didn't matter. Even though his words were painful, I knew how he felt about me. Surprisingly, I was cool, calm, and collected. It was a realization that no matter what I did or said it wasn't good enough. Mitch bullied and enjoyed his control of others both physically and mentally. Maybe, in his warped mind, he thought that his severe and strict behavior toward me made me a man. I tolerated these hostile actions, but I hoped and prayed that Mother, Susan, and Ronnie were never victims of his explosive temper or unfair tactics.

We returned from the store, and everything was in place, and the camp looked neat and clean. I figured that the men prolonged work and gave their wives an excuse that they needed to spend the night at camp. Then, they stayed at the camp and drank alcohol, gambled, and told nasty jokes. As night fell, they became rowdy, told jokes and bragged about their sexual prowess. I stayed in the sleeping area of the camp. I sat on a bunk until supper.

Paradoxically, Mitch had a few good qualities. He was the camp cook. He prepared meals at our house too when Mother worked late. Of course, Mrs. Rosie cooked us meals when Mitch worked overtime and weekends. He always kept a freezer full of wild game and garden vegetables.

That evening, Mitch prepared deer steak, potatoes, beans, corn, and sweet tea. After we ate, Mitch said, "You and Charley clear the table and wash dishes. When you've finished doing that, I want you to bed."

I listened, said nothing, and obeyed orders. I wanted to salvage the weekend without further conflicts. I trod lightly and kept my mouth shut. There was no sense arguing with Mitch because he played a rigged game. Besides, he was my stepfather, and I was taught to respect elders.

As I returned to my bunk, men played cards and drank. Charley had a knife in which he sharpened. Then, he whittled a stick and trapped the shavings into a newspaper. I encountered Charley at the Camp before and found him arrogant. He had hate and contempt for city boys. He was a brown-nose who undermined my efforts and promoted himself with snide remarks. I held my tongue and played the role of the peacemaker.

I was concerned because I feared a bedwetting incident, so decided not to sleep. If I had an accident, I was degraded, embarrassed, and teased which was too traumatic. I hoped and prayed that I didn't fall asleep. Charley went to bed, snored and released stomach gas. I thought to myself, what an uncouth and deplorable character.

The men in the kitchen became rowdier and louder as the liquor flowed. One of the men suggested that they go to Eagle Lake and pick up Delores. He said that she was a woman who made dreams come true for ten dollars. Also, he offered that she lived in a trailer near the Fin and Feather Store in the Eagle Lake Area. I was surprised that Mitch wasn't involved in this drunken, misguided mission.

I looked up from my bunk and noticed lizards and geckos as they raced across the ceiling. I tossed and turned for hours with the sounds of the ubiquitous buzz of mosquitoes. After what seemed like hours, nature called. I dressed and walked into the dining room area where Mitch sat at the kitchen table. He held a glass of Jim Beam in his left hand and a cigar in a makeshift, over-filled ashtray. His eyes were half-closed, and his body wavered back and forth. He was in a drunken stupor.

When he noticed that I was in the kitchen, he wheeled around and addressed me in an agitated tone. "Why in the hell or you up at this late hour?"

"I need to go to the bathroom."

"We don't have any bathrooms except for Mother Nature outside."

"Yes, I know, but I'm going to need some toilet tissue."

"Look in the kitchen cabinet and get a roll of toilet paper, do your business and hurry up and go back to bed."

The coolness of the night refreshed my sweaty body as I opened the front door. The stars were bright and twinkled throughout the entire night sky. I heard thousands of bullfrogs as they croaked in the bayou in conjunction with the incessant buzzing of mosquitoes. I was concerned for my safety, by the eerie sounds that came from both the bayou and the woods. I felt like thousands of eyes stared at me. I had visions of rattlesnakes that slithered in the nearby dense woods. For this reason, I dared not venture into the unsafe environs of the forest. Instead, I located a safe spot on the edge of the gravel as a restroom site. However, as I lifted my shirt and pulled down my pants, the mosquitoes swooped in and attacked my exposed body parts. The mosquitoes feasted and enjoyed a midnight buffet at my expense. After I finished, I covered everything well with gravel and returned to my bunk.

As the hours dragged by, I fought the urge and stayed awake. It was about 2:00 or 3:00 am when the men returned from their outing. They beeped, and I heard as they called for Mitch to come outside and see something appalling. My first thought was that they'd brought the woman back to the camp. However, it wasn't long before I realized that my preconceived notion wasn't the case. I soon discovered that I was involved in the controversy that brewed outside.

"DAVID LEE! Get your sorry ass up and come out here now."

He yelled so loudly that an awakened Charley inquired as to what had occurred outside.

"Go back to sleep Charley. They're calling for me, and it doesn't involve you."

I went outside and to my dismay, was confronted by an irate Mitch. His face was red with fury and his eyes pierced through me. He paced in a back and forth agitated motion which reminded me of a restless tiger that was ready to attack. I was scared and intimidated by his demeanor.

He screamed, "You're a sorry little bastard, I can't believe that you shit in front of the camp where people have to walk and drive."

46

One of the men had his truck lights that shone on the area in question, and it looked disgusting. The wind scattered the toilet paper from the original corner area of the parking lot. The paper was strewn and scattered over much of the camp parking lot. The men were embarrassed as Mitch cursed and insulted me. I was numbed and depressed from lack of sleep and the earlier incident with Mitch.

I felt defeated and embarrassed. To make matters worse, I saw Charley as he stood in the camp doorway and listened and digested what had occurred.

Mitch yelled, "Clean it up! Go and get a shovel and dig a hole and bury it all."

After I buried the waste and paper in the woods, I cleaned the shovel and returned to my bunk. Charley sat with a smirk on his face. Then, he stood up in front of his bed and confronted me and laughed. He put his hands on his side and approached me with an arrogant smile.

"It looks like city boys just don't get it. I can't believe that you went to the bathroom in the middle of the parking lot."

"Charley, I'm mad right now, and you need to be quiet. It's obvious that you're trying to rub salt in the wounds. Don't say anything else to me. I've had enough, and I'm not taking any more. Shut up!"

Charley's mouth fell open, and he looked like a deer caught in the headlights. He sat down on his bunk shocked and at a loss as what to say. After a few minutes, he slipped under his covers and with his back to me settled in for the night.

I stared at the camp ceiling as thoughts raced through my mind. Among them was the realization that I felt rotten that Charley angered me. I remembered

47

the verse from the Gospel of St. Mark that stated, "Blessed are the meek, for they shall inherit the Earth." Also, I gained strength in the Bible verse. "Blessed are the persecuted for righteousness' sake; for theirs is the Kingdom of Heaven." I felt a warm, positive feeling and newfound inner strength. I recited my prayers and drifted off to sleep.

I was awakened by Mitch's directive, "Get up. Let's go."

I was about to panic as I ran my hand down under my bed covers and felt my sheets and underwear. Thank God, I was dry as a bone.

It was cool outside as we loaded our gear in the Jeep and departed. It was dark, and I felt disoriented as to what we were doing. Suddenly, Mitch parked on the side of the road. He grabbed his twelve-gauge Remington shotgun and headed into the woods. I remained in the Jeep. At daybreak, I sensed the layout and topography of the area. I surveyed my surroundings. I heard loud, successive blasts from a shotgun."

A few minutes later, Mitch ran up the Jeep and said, "Come with me." We returned to the area that adjoined his deer stand. There we discovered, within twenty-five yards, a slain spike with small horns of three inches. We dragged the deer from the woods and wrapped it in a tarp and loaded it into the Jeep.

Mitch said, "Let's get out of here before somebody comes." He walked back into the woods and returned with a burlap sack. The darkness prevented me from identifying its contents. Nonetheless, Mitch threw the burlap sack on top of the slain deer.

He sat in the Jeep and perspired as he took deep breaths. He gathered his thoughts as he plotted a plan. He smoked a cigar, steadied his nerves,

48

coughed, cleared his throat, and spat out a wad of phlegm. Then, we departed after he drank a generous swig of Jim Beam whiskey.

I tried to imagine how he was going to pull this off. I questioned his sanity because we had to drive by the game warden's house with an illegal deer in the back of the Jeep. I figured that Mitch was going to drive in an inconspicuous manner and wave as we departed. To my surprise, Mitch drove up to the game warden's house and stopped. A pack of inquisitive beagles and Walker hounds sniffed around our Jeep and barked. The game warden, Jim Anderson, and two others approached us with concerned looks.

Mitch jumped out of the Jeep and yelled, "Look what I killed!" I panicked and thought, Oh Lord, he has gone crazy, and we'll get arrested. I envisioned gun confiscations, fines, and possible jail time. However, Mitch was cool as a cucumber and celebrated in this challenging predicament.

He reached through the window in the tailgate of the Jeep and pulled out the mysterious burlap sack. He reached deep into the bottom and pulled out a huge swamp rabbit. He displayed it, as he waved it back and forth in the morning air. The pack of dogs with this revelation reacted with sheer, primitive bestiality. They jumped high into the air and scaled Mitch's body and attempted to dislodge the bloody rabbit from his hand. They growled, snapped, and barked in a feral and vicious fashion.

"I thought you guys might want this rabbit. It's fresh because I ran over it this morning. I hated to leave it on the side of the road for scavengers to eat. I'm out of ice, and it'd go bad before I could get it home. It would be great as a rabbit stew or fried for that matter," he suggested. The dogs surrounded the jeep like Indians around a wagon train of pioneers. However, it appeared that everybody accepted that the dogs smelled traces or remnants of the rabbit's body and blood.

I was rattled and left the scene of the crime. I exited the Jeep and walked around and scoped out the warden's property. Mitch was inside and drank coffee with the game warden and his friends. It was hard for me to comprehend his audacity and nerve.

There were four men of questionable character who participated in a loud and animated conversation at a nearby dog pen. I discovered that they had a raccoon in a penned enclosure. They placed dogs in one at a time to fight the raccoon. The raccoon whipped all comers, and the dogs cowed into submission. The men placed bets on each event. Their combative demeanor prompted me to return to the Jeep. Fortunately, Mitch returned to his vehicle in a matter of minutes, and we departed for home.

I learned valuable lessons:

1. It wasn't wise to judge an enemy by their size. The small raccoon was a prime example to qualify this statement, and the dogs undoubtedly seconded that motion.
2. Mitch was smart, crafty, and more treacherous than I envisioned. This incident reminded me of the old movie "Houdini" which starred Tony Curtis. Harry Houdini, early in his career, was a stand-up magician. He pulled rabbits out of a top hat and mesmerized and entertained others. Mitch performed his form of magic and pulled a rabbit out of a burlap sack. This feat, performed to the delight of the game warden and friends, brought rave review. In these scenarios, there were two different types of captivated audiences. However, both Mitch and Harry Houdini entertained and delighted. Also, they fooled people by a slight of hand. It was simply magical. *Abracadabra!*

CHAPTER 6
THE GOSPEL ACCORDING TO MRS. ROSIE

When I returned home from the deer camp, I was physically and mentally fatigued. I took a bath which was followed by a nap. My bed felt like a million dollars, and I felt secure in the confines of my bedroom. Mitch was in his bedroom presumably asleep. I hoped that he hadn't said anything to Mother about what happened at the deer camp over the weekend.

I took a two-hour nap and woke by the sound of noisy dishes. I smelled bacon and heard the soft singing of an old Negro spiritual in a sweet and melodic tone.

"A Little Talk with Jesus, Oh! A little walk with Jesus makes it right, all right. A little talk with Jesus makes it right all right, troubles of every kind. That little talk with Jesus makes it right."

I put on my clothes and headed for the kitchen. There I encountered the vivacious Mrs. Rosie who was a petite, Colored lady with big brown eyes and a contagious laugh. Mrs. Rosie cooked and cleaned on certain days as needed.

"Mrs. Rosie. Good Morning. How in the world have you been doing?"

A startled Mrs. Rosie replied, "David Lee, you almost gave me a heart attack. I didn't know that you were standing there. She put her left hand on her hip and gave me a stern look and pointed at me with her right index finger as to give me a stern lecture. Were you trying to sneak up and scare me?" She erupted into a loud and familiar laugh with her addictively raspy voice. I always enjoyed when Mrs. Rosie visited because she had a unique and captivating personality. As far as I was concerned, Mrs. Rosie was a part of our family.

"Where is little Ronnie?"

"I think that he's still in bed."

"OOH! Little Ronnie likes his sleep alright. Get him up, and I'll fry y'all some eggs to go with the bacon that I cooked."

I went to Ronnie's bedroom and said, "You need to get up and eat breakfast."

"David Lee, leave me alone. I'm too tired."

"I'll eat your breakfast if you don't get up soon."

I went to the bathroom and brushed my teeth. A few minutes later, Ronnie entered the bathroom with wide-opened eyes, big as silver dollars. He had a pillow tucked under his arm. Ronnie crawled into the tub and positioned his pillow. Then, he stretched out in the tub and fell asleep, and this wasn't the first incident of Ronnie being a sleepwalker.

"Mrs. Rosie, please come and see this. You're not going to believe what just happened."

Mrs. Rosie, not knowing what to expect, entered the bathroom. She was wild-eyed and bewildered as she surveyed the situation. She slapped her hands together and yelled, "Wake up little Ronnie it's time get on up."

Mrs. Rosie nestled Ronnie in her arms and accompanied him to the dining room. "You boys are going to be the death of me," she said.

52

I switched on our Zenith stereo walnut console and tuned in to WRBC radio station out of Jackson. The song that played was *"Roses are Red."*

"Mrs. Rosie, do you think that he's a great singer?"

Mrs. Rosie asked, "Who is that singer?"

"That's Bobby Vinton; he's one of the new teenage heartthrob singers." Mrs. Rosie responded, "Yes, he can sing. He has a beautiful voice. Of course, he can't sing as good as my favorite singer, Sam Cooke."

"Yes, I love Sam Cooke too! He's one of the best."

I ate breakfast, read the newspaper, and listened to the radio. Ronnie sat in the dining room and ate. However, he yawned repeatedly and cleared his head. Mrs. Rosie hummed along with the radio as she cleaned the kitchen.

Mother drove up and beeped the horn. We ran out and helped her unload groceries. It was great that we saw Mother this morning because she usually had insurance appointments. Occasionally, she rearranged her schedule and made time for us. Of course, this was possible when she worked in town.

"Well, hello, everybody," Mother said in a quiet voice." We'd better whisper because Mitch is asleep."

Ronnie ran to Mother and hugged her neck and said, "I love you big like the world Mama."

"I love you too sweetheart."

Susan called from Rice's Dress Shop and asked to borrow a few dollars to dine at the Glass Kitchen Restaurant. Mother told her that she'd loan her money and would bring the money to the restaurant. It was convenient that Mother met Susan because she had a hair appointment on Walnut Street.

"Mama, can I spend the night with Billy this Saturday night? I asked. I want to help him deliver Sunday newspapers."

"It's Ok with me as long as you finish your chores. Mitch is going to need help working in the garden, mowing grass, and shelling purple hull peas and snapping the green beans. Please make sure that you complete these tasks."

"Yes Ma'am. I'll make sure that I have done everything on my list. I want to accompany Billy on his paper route."

Ronnie turned on the TV set and watched Looney Tunes cartoons. However, the TV reception was deplorable. The horizontal was messed up, and the vertical screen was distorted and rolled over in a slow to rapid fashion. However, he watched his program and was engrossed as he stared at the screen. I extended the rabbit ears atop the TV Set and wrapped them in aluminum foil. I wanted a clearer reception. Also, I adjusted the knobs as I turned the vise pliers back and forth. Amazingly, the TV screen readjusted, and Ronnie observed Wile E. Coyote's unsuccessful attempt as he dropped an Acme anvil on the head of the Roadrunner. Ronnie watched his program and was oblivious to my efforts.

Mother kissed us both goodbye and departed to go downtown. I reluctantly grabbed a bag of butter beans and shelled them.

Mrs. Rosie said, "David Lee, I'm getting ready to go in a minute, but make sure that you finish your chores."

"Yes, ma'am. Don't worry; I'll finish all my work."

"Mrs. Rosie. Is that your new car parked out front?"

"It sure is my new car," she excitedly stated. "I bought it last week from my cousin Buster Lee. He lost his job at Crowley's Pool Hall and let me take up the payments."

"Is that a Ford?"

"It's a 1956 *Ford Fair Lane Victoria,*" she stated proudly.

"Do you know what F- O- R- D stands for?"

"No, I just thought it was a name. What does it stand for David Lee?"

"It means two things." I responded, "Fix-Or-Repair-Daily and Found-On-Road-Dead."

"Lord of Mercy." Mrs. Rosie laughed and said, "I hope neither one of those bad things happen to me or my car."

I suggested, "Let me help you get your belongings out because I want to get a good look at your beautiful car. I love a two-tone red and white car!"

Mrs. Rosie looked at me and said, "David Lee, you be careful now. I worry about you and your family." I nodded in agreement with her comment. Then, she waved goodbye and departed.

I noticed that Mitch was awake. He walked around the yard and checked on things. After a few minutes, he called out to me, "David Lee, come here!"

I went to the south corner of the house. Mitch surveyed and rubbed the surface of his "D" Class racing boat Big Daddy. He seldom raced and depended on friend Andy Sellers to run it for him. Most competitive boat races were at Eagle Lake and on the Vicksburg waterfront.

"Yes sir, did you want me?"

"Boy, you didn't sand this boat, and I told you that I wanted it done."

"I just haven't gotten around to it yet," I explained. I'll start on it now."

Mitch's face turned crimson red and perspiration beaded and rolled down his brow. He yelled, "I can't believe that you didn't sandpaper this damn boat! You didn't do what I told you to do."

Without warning, Mitch reached into the boat and pulled out a tree branch. He struck me hard across my back. The heavy impact of his swing shattered the stick into splintered pieces. I retreated through the back door. I stumbled through the hallway and went into the bathroom in great pain. My concern was a continued onslaught.

He started his Jeep which was music to my ears. The sound of shifted gears resounded as he drove away. I entered the living room, and Ronnie was on the couch. "David Lee, what was all that yelling and noise about?"

I shrugged my shoulders and indicated that I didn't know. At that moment, I knew that if I spoke that I'd start crying. I didn't want to upset Ronnie about what had happened.

I returned outside, confused, and sanded the boat for an hour. Then, I reentered the house and finished shelling a large bag of butter beans. I was befuddled and felt desperate and worked off nervous energy. My feelings were hurt more than the physical pain. Mitch's disrespect rattled me, and I questioned my worth as a person.

After I finished my chores, I took a bath and investigated the extent of my injuries. I looked in the mirror and saw that my back had a red mark the length of my hand. I soaked in the hot tub for forty-five minutes. I wasn't going to tell anyone what had happened. I kept the incident from Ronnie, Susan, and Mother.

I got out of the tub and dried my hair with a towel. I avoided the mirror because I felt ashamed. Involuntary tears poured down my face, and my throat felt as if it was on fire. I took deep breaths as my heart pounded like a bass drum.

I convinced myself that I needed emotional strength. It was inevitable, that future confrontations and dilemmas were imminent. I knew that with my family was where I belonged, but I feared Mitch. Furthermore, I believed that Mother, Susan, and Ronnie needed me. My course of action was to live one day at a time and let the pieces fall where they may. I had no other choice in the matter. I prayed, "Lord Jesus, please help me because I can't face Mitch alone."

CHAPTER 7
PAPER BOYS/JIM CROW

The remainder of the week, I stayed out of Mitch's way and avoided controversy. Also, I worked hard all week because I wanted to spend the night with Billy and accompany him on his paper route. On this outing, we rose at 3:00 am and went downtown to the Vicksburg Evening Post Building. The Sunday Edition was the most expensive and favorite paper of the week. Unfortunately, it was the bulkiest paper of the week and took several bicycle saddle bags to load. The saddlebags were attached to back seat, and leftover papers were carried in the basket on the handlebars or physically carried.

Billy arrived at my home in the early evening and verified that the plans hadn't changed. He asked if I still intended to spend the night and assist him on his paper route. Even though I'd mentioned this to Mother, I needed her confirmation. Mother and Mitch sat at the dining room table, and I approached them with nervous anticipation.

"May I still spend the night with Billy?"

"Have you completed all your work assignments for the week?"

"Yes Ma'am."

"Mitch is it OK with you if David Lee spends the night with Billy?"

Mitch stared out into space and looked disinterested and replied, "It's up to you Evelyn. He's your son. However, he'd better be back in the morning by 8:00 am. We're going to work in the garden." He added, "I do mean work."

"Do you understand what we're saying to you?"

"Yes Ma'am."

"Give me a goodbye kiss and behave yourself."

"Thanks, I'll see you in the morning," I said as I kissed Mother on the cheek.

Billy waited for me outside. We took my Mercury bicycle on this outing since my Sears Space Liner bicycle had a bent frame and a leaky tire. Billy rode a 24" Huffy bike.

When we entered Billy's house, the smell of dirty diapers was overwhelming. Their home teemed with children who laughed and played. The young Catholic family consisted of nine children whose ages ranged from one to fifteen. Also, Mrs. Nancy Jo expected another child in a few months. They were athletic, robust, and the picture of health. For example, when their mother called the children for meals they ran to the kitchen and resembled a thundering herd of cattle.

We stayed up and watched TV until about 11:00 pm. All the small kids went to bed, and Mrs. Nancy Jo sat on the patio and relaxed and read a book. We told her goodnight and asked if she had an alarm clock. We needed an early start.

"What time are you guys getting up?"

"We're getting up at 3:00 am."

"OK, it's getting late, so you better hit the sack," she replied.

Mrs. Nancy Jo told me, "I forgot to mention to you earlier, that your brother sang this evening on the hill. It sounded like he was crying when he finished singing. I don't mean to sound nosey, but is everything alright with you and your family?"

"Everything is alright as far as I know. If there's ever a problem in the future, then I'll let you know. Thank you so much for asking."

"Well, if y'all ever need help with anything, then please feel free to call us."

I went to Billy's bedroom, and there were three sets of bunk beds. The younger kids slept in bassinets and baby cribs that were placed all over the house. The youngest slept in their parents' bedroom. The girls had a bedroom with two bunk beds. It was a small three-bedroom house, but the children were well-nourished, had a roof over their heads, and were loved.

I made sure that I didn't drink anything late at night and prevented unwanted accidents. Babies cried and yelled during the night in short intervals. It was like a cycle in that there was dead silence and then a baby cried, which triggered a chain reaction, and the rest followed suit. I thought about my family and prayed to God for their protection. Also, I prayed for things to change for the better. I fell asleep after I tossed and turned for about an hour.

The next sound I heard was the loud and discordant alarm clock. It was 3:00 am and time to go. Billy, Sammy, and I rushed outside and welcomed the warm, sultry, morning air. We had two bicycles and three bodies. Since I was the lightest in weight Sammy rode my bike. I straddled the handlebars and went down hills and on flat land. However, I walked whenever we climbed hills. Billy rode his bike, and we switched our planned configuration when needed.

We began the adventure and positioned ourselves on bikes and turned on mounted lights. We propelled down Pemberton Street at a breakneck pace. We negotiated a sharp corner as we turned on Sky Farm Avenue. I hung onto the handlebars with all my strength. I crouched low because I was cognizant of the fact that Sammy needed a clear vision. We laughed about the high speed and daring as we negotiated the first corner. After the episode, I looked forward to the first inclining hill so that I could safely walk.

It was spooky and eerie as we passed the Cedar Hill Cemetery fence. Sky Farm Avenue was deserted and deadly quiet this morning. Occasionally, dogs barked, and cats screeched. They were the only signs of living entities.

A mile into our journey, we encountered a stretch of inclining hills on Farmer Street. We alternated as we pedaled and walked up hills or scaled them at an angle. When the hill was steep, we suffered. We all assisted and laboriously pushed the bikes up the hill.

After two miles into our journey, the hills subsided. At that time, we sped down Openwood and Jackson Streets. It was reminiscent of race car drivers Parnelli Jones and A.J.Foyt as they competed in the USAC National Sprint Car Series Championships. We turned left on Cherry Street and continued about a half a mile until we reached the Vicksburg Evening Post Building. It was 4:00 am when we arrived. There were eight or ten boys who waited in line and received Sunday morning papers. Billy got in line and received his stack of newspapers. As soon as he returned with his papers, we folded and placed rubber bands around them. There was frivolity, camaraderie, and boisterous antics, and chatter emoted by the group. However, it was all in fun, and it was good to visit classmates that we hadn't seen all summer. Overall, we all enjoyed the banter.

We loaded the newspapers and pushed, mounted, and pedaled our bicycles and achieved momentum. Our bikes headed north down Cherry Street. We began the paper route with enthusiasm and delivered papers in the Cherry and Grove Street areas. The old homes scared and intimidated us as we ran and crisscrossed from yard to yard. We snaked our way up and down empty side streets and alleys. We threw newspapers on front porches with special care and avoided breaking porch items. Eventually, we worked our way to St. Aloysius Catholic High School on Clay Street. As we headed east on Clay Street, the paper route became less burdensome. We delivered papers to commercial, well-lighted businesses. A few of these were Koestler's Bakery, Gibson's, and the Rose Oil Station. Our stomachs growled from the aroma of the freshly baked bread from Koestler's Bakery.

We worked hard and at a rapid pace. After we finished the route, we were famished. We decided that we'd dine at the Vicksburg Café on Washington Street. A combination of hard work and the bakery smell catapulted our hunger levels into the stratosphere.

I hadn't eaten at the Vicksburg Café and was excited to sample their culinary specialties. As we arrived at the restaurant, I found it strange that there were two separate entry doors. One was for "Colored" customers, and the other was for "White" patrons. Also, inside the restaurant, there was a middle section which structurally separated the Races. This middle section was the kitchen with cooks and waitresses who served patrons from both sides. It struck me as strange that Colored and White customers sat on stools at opposing counters in the same facility. I thought that it was bizarre that we sat in the same dining room, but not next to each other. I recalled that Mr. Harley my Social Studies teacher had lectured on the "Plessy vs. Ferguson" Supreme Court decision that set up a doctrine of "Separate but Equal." The Races had segregation in the same facility. I remembered that he said that these were called "Jim Crow" Laws.

The smell of bacon, sausage, eggs, grits, biscuits, and toast stimulated my taste buds. We chose a breakfast special that consisted of two eggs, two types of meat, grits, and toast or biscuits. I ordered two fried eggs over easy, extra crispy bacon and sausage patties, buttered grits, biscuits, and brown gravy. I had a large glass of chocolate milk that complemented my breakfast. We were in a great mood because we worked hard and rewarded ourselves with good food. Billy picked up the tab because he was appreciative that we helped.

Two men in the booth behind us argued about the upcoming college football season.

The first man asked, "What in the hell is a buckeye anyway?"

The second responded, "You'll know what a buckeye is when the Ohio State Buckeyes led by Head Coach Woody Hayes wins the 1962 National Championship."

"It's not going to happen. The road to the National Championship goes through Oxford, Mississippi, and the Ole Miss Rebels under Quarterback Glynn Griffing and Head Coach Johnny Vaught," The first man responded.

"The only thing that's going to the University of Mississippi is that Negro James Meredith when he enrolls in the fall semester to take classes. Can you believe that this is going to happen?"

The first man stated, "I don't think so! Governor Ross Barnett will have something to say to the Kennedy brothers about that. He'll set their asses straight."

"I hope that you are right because this could be a bad situation. I don't know why this Colored boy would want to attend our college anyway. They have their schools, and he could go to one of his own Negro colleges like Jackson State or Alcorn A & M."

"It's probably one of those outside COFO agitators or the NAACP that's stirring him up and paying him to go to Ole Miss. They're just trying to rile up the citizens of the State of Mississippi."

Their conversation was too loud and political for my taste and as we departed the restaurant patrons ranted and raved over other political and sports issues. The essence of that delicious breakfast lingered as we left the restaurant at 6:00 am. The trip home was faster since most of the journey was down-hill.

As we arrived at Pemberton Street, we dismounted from the bicycles and pushed them the rest of the way up the hill. All that food that we consumed rumbled in our guts as we strained from physical exertion. It was inevitable that someone was going to lose their manners. Billy launched the first stink bomb which was followed by a loud fart from me.

We yelled, "Scobey" to the tops of our voices.

Sammy said, "I called 'Scobey' before either one of you, so y'all come here and take your medicine like men."

We disagreed with his assertions. Furthermore, as a rebuttal we claimed, "NO, Sammy, we said 'Scobey' first."

The doctrine of might makes right settled the futile argument. Sammy was larger and stronger than us. For this reason, we accepted his unjust decision.

Also, we adhered to the sanctity of the rules of the game of "Scobey." We received our punitive justice. I prepared myself mentally and received lots of pain. The man-child Sammy administered pokes to us swiftly and judicially, and my arm hurt, but it could've been worse.

Sammy was a sophomore football player at St. Aloysius High School. He started on the varsity as a freshman. This upcoming season he was touted as an "All-District" starting lineman. He was a gentle giant who was a good brother to Billy. Because Mrs. Nancy Jo told me that Ronnie was sad, I resolved myself to the notion that I needed to be a better brother. I thanked Billy for buying breakfast. I checked the time and realized that it was 6:30 am. Mitch, Ronnie, and I had an hour and a half before we departed to work in the garden. I hoped and prayed that today was a good day. However, in my heart of hearts, I had serious doubts.

CHAPTER 8
FLY AWAY

As I inched closer to my home, I thought that I wanted a day without stress. Hopefully, when I worked in the garden, I received much-needed exercise. Also, this was a potential opportunity to mend fences with Mitch. I had to stay positive and live one day at a time. Since I was thirteen years of age, I had no choice in the matter. I loved my mother and wanted to remain with my family. Maybe, if things worked out, Mitch would tolerate me one day.

My main thought as I returned home was that I needed a bath. I noticed that the house was dark and everyone was asleep. I tried to enter through the front door, but it was locked. I walked around the house and realized everyone was asleep. Then, I went to the back door, which was the kitchen door. I remembered that we had problems with the lock on the door. I turned the doorknob and pushed on it, but it didn't budge. I twisted and pushed a little harder and with more conviction. However, I was not successful. I stood back from the back door and surveyed the rear of the house to determine if anyone had awakened. Thankfully, I hadn't awakened a soul with the noise that I made. I knew that it wasn't wise to awaken my family. My choices were limited. Either I waited for someone to awaken or pushed on the back door. I gave the door one more aggressive push. The door flew open as I exerted pressure. I lost my balance and tripped head first onto the kitchen floor. I knocked over empty Coca-Cola bottles that were stacked next to the inside of the door. The noise of the door opened the door, and the loud sound of broken bottles didn't go unnoticed.

I struggled and got back on my feet and straightened coke bottles. An angry Mitch confronted me.

"What in the hell is going on?"

I looked apologetic and before I said a word he erupted. He grabbed my collar and slapped me. I landed underneath the dining room table. As I stood up, he hovered over me with a belt in his right hand. He reached down and grabbed me by the nape of my neck with his left hand. He lashed me across my back and legs with his belt. As he swung his belt wildly, I held my hands up in a defensive position. He twirled me around with such force that I tripped over a dining room table chair. He lifted me off the floor and rammed me into the wall. He threw me so hard against the wall that my elbow and back went through the sheetrock. As I fell to the floor, he slapped me across my head.

Mother and Susan heard the commotion and ran into the dining room. Susan arrived first and confronted Mitch.

Susan yelled, "Quit! You're going to hurt him!"

Mitch appeared startled and unsure of what to say. However, he released his grip on me and walked back to his bedroom. Mother met him in the hallway and told him that they needed to talk.

Susan said, "David Lee. Are you alright? I can't believe that he hit you like that. Let's go and clean you up in the bathroom. We'll talk later."

I nodded my head in agreement and entered the bathroom. As I investigated my injuries, I was joined by Susan with an ice bag for my busted lip. There were additional red lash marks on my neck and back. On the top of my forehead, there were several knots. There were red lash marks on my arms and legs. Most of my shirt buttons were torn off, and my pockets were ripped off. Susan looked at me with pity in her eyes. She returned to her bedroom with tear-filled eyes.

I took a hot bath, and as I reclined in the tub, I heard Mother and Mitch's conversation. She told Mitch that she didn't appreciate the way that he manhandled me. However, she had no problem with him correctly administering punishment. She stressed that her children were well-behaved and deserved respectful treatment. She said that if the two of them expected a successful marriage, that these episodes had to end. She reminded him that when they got married, informed that it was a group deal and the children were part of the bargain.

After I left the bathroom, I met with Susan.

"Let's go outside and talk because I don't want anybody to hear our conversation."

We walked outside and strolled down the street. Susan was sad and worried. She controlled her emotions, but I knew that she was going to tell me something important.

"What did you want to discuss? What is it?"

Susan replied, "I thought that I could live with Mother and Mitch, but this summer has proven that it's impossible. Last year when I stayed with Sarah and graduated from Leland High School, I had a boyfriend from Greenville. We wrote letters and had long distance conversations all summer. We've become close, and I'm considering going steady with him. Also, I'm going to enter a beauty pageant this summer. For these reasons, I'm moving back to Greenville to live with Sarah. I'll get a job and my place eventually. Sadly, I'll have to give up my job at Rice's Dress Shop and leave family and friends."

She continued, "I love my family with all my heart, but I can't tolerate Mitch because I refuse to live with an overbearing alcoholic. I wished that Mother would admit that she made a mistake and ended it. Promise me that if he attacks you again that you'll defend yourself. He has no right to put his hands on you like that. If you feel endangered, then you need to fight back. I'm concerned that he'll hurt you."

"I know that what you're telling me is true and for my good. I promise you that if Mitch hits me again that I'll try and defend myself."

"Please do that for me. Mitch is an evil man. I know that if I stay in this house that something bad is going to happen to me because we hate each other."

"When will you be leaving?"

"I'm going to leave tomorrow morning. I've been planning this move for two weeks."

"I wish you wouldn't go, but I understand. It's probably the best decision that you can make. Please keep in touch and don't forget us."

"Are you kidding? I'll always be your sister, and you'll always be my brother. One day in the future, we'll look back on this with different eyes. Maybe one day we can live together without Mitch in our lives."

"By the way, thanks for getting Mitch off me. You were like my guardian angel. I appreciate it."

"That's what loved ones do for each other. I know that you'd do the same for me."

"No doubt about it. We'll always be there for each other."

It became quiet as we both reflected and savored the moment. Then my thoughts returned to the reality of the moment. I had to face Mitch without Susan. She always made things better, and her enthusiasm and support were appreciated.

"Let's do this!" Susan blurted out.

"Do what? I'm confused".

"I've decided to take you and Ronnie on a picnic this afternoon. Later, we'll go swimming in the Redwood Pool. It'll be my going away present to the both of you."

"Come here Brother, and give me a big hug."

We embraced in the middle of Second Avenue. I looked forward to our planned activity. However, I was upset because of the departure of my beloved sister.

CHAPTER 9
GARDEN OF HADES

When we returned home, everything between Mother and Mitch had calmed down. He was in a good mood and readied to work outdoors.

"David Lee, go and wake up your brother because we need to work. We're leaving in thirty minutes. Also, get the hoes, shovels, gloves, and water cooler loaded in the Jeep, and I'll get the remainder."

"Okay," I responded in a confused manner. I thought to myself at least Mitch called me by my name and seemed civil. Maybe, Mother worked things out with him.

I went to Ronnie's bedroom, and he was soundly asleep. He slept through the incident that occurred earlier. That was unbelievable to me. I shook Ronnie's shoulders and awakened him, and he jumped straight up in his bed. He looked at me with a wild, vulnerable gaze that resembled a defenseless, subdued animal. Then, he dashed out of his room and into Mother's bedroom.

"Well good morning, sweetheart. Did you have a good night's sleep?"

"Not really, Mama. It's like morning came too soon."

"Goodness." Mother said when she hugged Ronnie, and the back of his tee shirt rose and exposed his back.

"What is wrong, Mama?" Ronnie said as he pulled down his tee shirt.

71

"It's all that blonde, thick hair on your back. That means that one day you're going to be a rich man."

"Momma, when I become rich, I'm going to buy you a beautiful mansion and a Cadillac."

"Sweetheart, you don't have to buy me expensive things."

"Mama, I want to offer you stuff one day."

"In the future, you'll make me happy if you become a decent, working man."

"Mama, I'll do whatever it takes to make you happy. However, since you mentioned working, do I have to go and work in the garden this morning? I don't want to go."

"Well, you're ten years old and need to start helping David Lee with chores. You need to go and get ready sweetheart."

I walked back into the house after I loaded the Jeep. Ronnie skipped a bath and was ready, and Mitch gathered things together. Mother hugged me and assured me that everything was alright. Those words comforted me, and I felt rejuvenated. I was prepared to put in a hard day's work. She kissed us and waved goodbye as we boarded the Jeep.

We arrived at the garden, which was a half-acre plot of land. The garden was in the Harrison and Maxwell Streets area. Located by a railroad track, it was in a wooded area. We planted seeds in March and had worked in the garden sometimes as often as twice a week. We labored the spring and summer and ensured that we had a successful crop.

The work paid off, and we had a freezer packed full of vegetables. Every day we ate corn, tomatoes, okra, and cucumbers in some form or fashion. Also, we had snap-beans, purple-hull peas, and butterbeans. In the back rows of the garden, there were watermelon and cantaloupe patches. I monitored the growth of the vegetables. They required constant attention and intense labor. We pulled and hoed weeds, pruned plants, tied stalks, removed dead parts of plants, sprayed and dusted for insects, and fertilized. Of course, we picked vegetables daily to prevent them from rotting on the vine. We arrived at the garden with burlap sacks, paper bags, boxes, and buckets to load vegetables.

Mitch placed Ronnie on the third row of beans and peas. Ronnie picked and pulled weeds around the plants. He put me on the first and second rows, and I removed weeds and pruned the okra and tomato plants. I was glad that I'd worn a long sleeve shirt with gloves because the okra plants were prickly. Mitch checked out the garden and evaluated the status of the plants and their overall condition. Also, he removed corn from the stalks and loaded them into burlap sacks. We picked most of the corn at the beginning of July, but there were still a few remaining stalks.

After two hours of intense and concentrated work, we took a water break. Mitch and Ronnie ate apples and slices of rat trap cheese with Ritz crackers. I wasn't hungry since I ate the big breakfast hours earlier. The sun baked down on us, and the high humidity made us uncomfortable. I knew that as we returned from the break, that the rising temperatures created a challenging work situation. We visited the water cooler frequently as sweat poured from our bodies. We wrung out our shirts and bandanas. My baseball cap was saturated with perspiration and was stained halfway down the bill.

As the morning progressed, the oven heat sweltered, and humidity was a formidable foe. The unrelenting heat settled between the rows of vegetables and baked the plants and dirt. As an indolent wind stalled, I heard Ronnie. He whimpered and cried as he worked in the hot confines of the third row. It was monotonous labor with a presence of wasps, sweat-bees, horse-flies, and other insects. Breathing was difficult as the dust stirred into the air by a combination of slight wind and body movements.

Suddenly, Ronnie cried out, "I'm hot and miserable and want to go home!"

I ran over to Ronnie and told him, "Please do your work quietly. You don't want to get in trouble."

"I don't care. I want to go home now."

Mitch asked, "Is that Ronnie I hear singing the *'Whining for a Tit Blues?'*"

"Mitch, I just want to go home. I hate doing this. It's hot, and I'm tired and miserable."

Mitch continued his teasing tirade. "Ronnie, you need to grow up and quit being such a baby. You need to toughen up. Because if you don't stop being such a crybaby, then one day you'll grow up and become a damn queer!"

"What is that? What is a queer?" Ronnie asked.

"Never mind that, just keep working."

"Why don't you take a short break and drink some water? I'll work on your row until you come back."

"Thanks, David Lee. That might do me some good."

74

We worked an additional hour in this hot environment. Then, Mitch told us that it was time to depart. We stopped working and loaded vegetables and tools which was welcome news for us because the day had become unbearable. I felt empathy for Ronnie but dared not speak in his defense because of retribution from Mitch.

Mitch stoically said, "I promised your Mother that I'd get you piss-ants home in time for church services. Hurry up, and let's get back to the house."

As we prepared to depart, I noticed that Mitch lit a cigar as Ronnie fell asleep and perspired profusely. I placed my bandana under the water cooler spigot. After I soaked my bandana with cold water, I wiped off my neck and brow. Then, I put ice in my bandana and held it on Ronnie's hot forehead as he slept in the Jeep. I picked him up and put him across my lap as his hands and legs dangled. I rolled down the passenger window and fanned Ronnie with my baseball cap. Mitch left the vehicle and retrieved a garden tool that was at the end of the second row. The Jeep idled, and the motor knocked as if it would go dead at any moment. A freight train passed and scattered dust, debris, and odorous diesel fumes. The train's horn blared and made a thunderous sound. The ground rumbled and vibrated under the Jeep. It was as if we had experienced an earthquake. The Jeep emitted gas and oil vapors from an overheated motor. These emissions spilled into the cab. The thick and opaque smoke filled the vehicle's cab with a suffocating smell. I felt as though I was on the verge of a heatstroke because what I viewed next was surreal. I looked from the Jeep and saw garden rows that sweltered in the heat. Dust rose from the bottom to the top of the plants and swirled in an unorthodox fashion from row to row. The sun struggled and partially shone thru the thick layer of smoke that settled from the top row of the plants. A mirage appeared that wasn't of this world. Suddenly, a shadowy figure approached us from the garden. It carried a large tool in one hand. I squinted and strained my eyes and got a clearer vision because of temporary darkness

75

and an ember of fire emanated from the being's mouth. As the dark figure approached, feet dragged and created a trail of dust and smoke. Was this who I thought it was? I shivered because the vision frightened me. I had to listen to the church sermon today with baited ears and hang onto every word. My vivid imagination needed to be kept in check. "Praise the Lord!"

CHAPTER 10
REDWOOD REVENGE

Sunday afternoon, I sat in the front pew at Good Hope Baptist Church. The preacher was in rare form, and my spirits uplifted by his sermon on the Book of Acts. After church services, we anticipated Susan's going-away picnic and the Redwood pool excursion. We boarded her *Desoto*, and we were on our way. Susan packed a picnic basket with sandwiches, chips, and sodas. We stopped at a roadside park on Highway 61 and enjoyed lunch before we went swimming. It was a beautiful day for a picnic and Sharon's departure tomorrow morning was the only thing that prevented the day from being perfect.

We consumed lunch and then took a hike and explored the nearby woods. We came across a cluster of tall oak trees covered in buck vines. Somebody cut a few loose, and they were ready for use. Susan grabbed the vine and walked it back up the hill. While she held the vine, I pulled her back and released her. She soared high over a hollow. Within minutes, we all located suitable and stable vines. We swung into the woods in a Tarzan-and-Jane-like fashion. We limited our play on the vines to twenty minutes because the novelty wore off. We continued our journey and came upon strange fruit that was on the ground next to a gnarly, old tree.

Ronnie asked, "What is this green thing that looks like a lumpy green orange with wrinkles." Susan replied, "Those are crab apples."

"They come from an Orange Osage tree that's referred to in the South as bois d'arc. They use the wood of that tree to make archery bows," I said.

"How in the world did you know that?" Susan inquired.

"Daddy taught me. He was fascinated with the skill of a famous archer named Howard Hill. He was interested in archery through him and made a bow from the tree."

"Daddy was so smart, and I remember that he made lamps and wall clocks from cypress stumps. He made a coffee table, clay model cars, and he even cut patterns for Mother to make dresses for Sarah and me."

"I miss Daddy. I wish that he and Mother hadn't divorced," I said.

"Mitch doesn't love us," Ronnie said with tears in his eyes.

Susan added, "The situation is what it is. We're just going to have to make the best of it."

She embraced Ronnie and comforted him with soothing words. Then, we ventured deeper into the woods until we reached a clearing in which we saw two antebellum mansions. They faced each other and were about one hundred yards apart with impressive pecan, magnolia, and moss-draped oak trees. These stately mansions appeared regally frozen in time.

"I never knew that these homes existed. Do you know the story behind them?" Susan asked.

"These homes are the Blakely and the Dorman mansions," I replied. "They're haunted. In fact, there are old slave quarters behind the Dorman home."

I knew that we were unwelcomed when I noticed dogs approaching us from the Blakely home. They barked and growled at us in an aggressive manner. I recalled from visiting David Blakely three months ago that his dogs were vicious.

The dogs were at a distance but impressively gained on us. We laughed at the face of danger and ran back to the trail from whence we came. We sped through poison ivy, sticker bushes, beggar lice, kudzu vines, and spider webs and distanced ourselves from the pursuing carnivores. We sprinted down the path all the way to the picnic area. I was surprised that Ronnie ran so fast.

Upon our return, we cleaned up the picnic area. We loaded the car and waited for thirty minutes before we departed. We sat down on the picnic bench to catch our breath. Also, we needed to let our food settle before we went to the Redwood swimming pool. I seized the opportunity and told one of my patented jokes.

"I have a joke to tell you both. It's called the 'Most Beautiful Baby Contest.' Have y'all heard it?" I asked.

Ronnie replied, "Well, it'd better be funny."

"The joke is funny because the joke concerns you," I said as Ronnie grimaced and gave me a cold stare.

"There was a baby who was ugly, but his mother thought that he was beautiful. She signed him up for the 'Most Beautiful Baby Contest' held at the city auditorium. The auditorium was across the street from where they lived. It snowed that night with blizzard-like conditions. The other contestants were unable to travel in the snow storm. Consequently, the mother and baby who resided across the street from the auditorium were the only ones in attendance. Her baby was the only contestant. Can you guess what happened? Well, he was so ugly that the judges gave him the second place!" I blurted out with gusto.

Ronnie asked, "Are you saying that I was that ugly baby?"

Susan laughed and said, "Ronnie, he's kidding. You know that I always thought that you were a good-looking kid. You resemble that handsome actor, Tab Hunter."

"Yes, and you were 'Mr. Physique' in 1958," I sarcastically added.

"Well, at least I don't resemble a walking-stick or praying mantis. Mr. Thin Man," Ronnie said.

"Stop bickering you two, I mean it!" Susan checked the time on her Lady Omega watch and asked, "Are you guys ready to go swimming?"

"Yes!" We replied.

We sped down the road to the Redwood Pool, and this was the last outing with Susan for a while, and I was sad. However, our anticipation and excitement grew as we drove up to the Redwood Pool. The parking area was full, and there were people everywhere. The Redwood Pool was a swimming hole converted from a pond. There were twenty or thirty inner tubes one could rent from the facility, a diving board, and a giant sliding board. The pool was cordoned off by a stretched fiberglass rope that had spaced red and white safety floats attached. It was obvious that you wouldn't want to venture on the other side of the floats because it had a snaky type atmosphere.

A few adults were in lawn chairs, and the sound of music blared from their transistor radios. The diving board was the focal point of interest. There was a constant stream of ten to twelve swimmers who waited in line to take a turn jumping off. Swimmers in the water watched and rated their dives and jumps. Everyone judged their efforts and either praised or booed. There were a few skilled divers who performed front and back dives. Some Jumpers executed cannonballs and can-openers. The can-opener competition was the highlight from the diving board. The crowd rated the candidates by the heights they splashed with thunderous applause. Conversely, a weak splash earned catcalls and vocal degradation.

After we witnessed the exciting can-opener competition, we slid down the giant sliding board. The sliding board had a garden hose placed on the top area, and it kept the board slick. This constant stream of water lubricated the slide and gave us propulsion as we jetted off the slide. We took turns, and we went down in an upright position and on our backs. Daredevils opted for a head-first diving position. sons. We slid down the board, entered the water, and resurfaced invigorated. Then we swam to the ladder and exited the pool. I practiced a few preliminary sliding rounds into the cool depths of the muddy water. I timed my slides near where Ronnie surfaced. Of course, I wanted to swamp him. He warned me that I needed to stop my antics because he swallowed water. However, I attempted to splash him one more time. The music from the radio played *"Speedy Gonzales"* by Pat Boone as he launched off from the sliding board. In the excitement of the moment, I released too early and landed on top of Ronnie as he surfaced. The force of my momentum and weight planted him into the depths of the muddy bottom. I felt horrible for what I had done! Ronnie resurfaced and cried and spat out water. I assisted him to the side of the pool and helped him up the ladder.

He cried out after he plopped down on the ground, "I'm telling mama, and she's going to get you good."

"I'm sorry, please forgive me."

"No, I won't forgive you because you did it on purpose."

We sat there in our solitude, and neither one of us spoke. My thoughts were that I shouldn't have mistreated my brother. I realized that whatever punishment my mother imposed upon me was justified. I realized that what I did was wrong and inexcusable. Also, my reckless action caused my brother emotional pain, and this was a valuable lesson in life from which to learn. I needed to nurture a positive influence in my brother's life.

Susan walked on the other side of the pool with a group of admiring young boys who followed closely behind. She was shapely in her swimsuit, and the male patrons watched her every movement. Ronnie and I had worn cut-off jeans and tattered football jerseys. When we got out of the pool, we chilled to the bone. Immediately, our teeth shattered and our bodies shivered. Our best option was to remain in the water until time to leave.

However, Ronnie's swimming session for the day was over because of my dumb prank. I stayed with him and offered comfort. I was an unwelcome guest, and he didn't speak or acknowledged my existence. After about an hour, it was time to depart. I borrowed a quarter from Susan for a snack. I purchased a moon pie and a hostess cupcake at the concession stand. I was hungry and bought both.

"Ronnie, would you like either one of these?" I offered.

"David Lee. Your generosity isn't going to work. I'm still telling Mother what you did, and she's going to beat you."

Susan asked, "What's going on between you two?"

"I messed up. I was trying to splash Ronnie at the sliding board, and I landed on him and hurt him. What I did was wrong."

Ronnie looked at me and said, "You should've thought about that before you did it."

"You boys need to help each other, and you shouldn't be fighting over silly things like this. There will be tough times ahead, so you'd better have each other's back. Before you boys board my car, make sure that you've dried off and that you sit on towels. I don't want my car seats to get wet."

On the way home, we stuck our heads out the window and hummed into the warm wind. Also, we cupped hands and caught the wind. The sun sank in the west, and we observed low clouds as they hovered over the Yazoo River and Lake Centennial. There was a swirled mixture of orange, blue, and white in the distant afternoon sky. The complement of the forest green grass and trees blended with the soft pastel colors and created another one of God's majestic and glorious works of art.

CHAPTER 11
GENTLEMEN PREFER BLONDES

We returned home from swimming in the early evening hours. Ronnie informed Mother of my wrongdoings. She was disappointed by my immature and reckless behavior. She asked me if I had apologized to Ronnie. I told her that I had, but he hadn't forgiven me for my misguided transgression. She followed me into my bedroom and told me that my actions could've hurt Ronnie. She reminded me that I should be protective and supportive of my brother. I replied that what I had done was wrong and that I deserved punishment. She returned with a belt and told me to turn around. She administered a few well-deserved swats. Ronnie was in his bedroom, no doubt listening and was delighted over my punishment. Later, I left a hostess cupcake outside his closed bedroom door as a peace offering.

I tossed and turned all night in a cold sweat. The thought of Susan's departure put me in a nervous state of mind. I dreamt during the night that Susan changed her mind and decided to stay. I awakened this blue Monday with the realization that I was the victim of a pipe dream. The reality of the matter was that she'd depart within the hour.

I turned on the radio to a shocking news announcement! Marilyn Monroe was found dead in her apartment in Los Angeles this morning. It was unbelievable! She was one of my favorite actresses, and I enjoyed the film "Bus Stop." I remembered that she had married Yankee legend, Joe DiMaggio. This heartbreaking news shocked me to my core.

My thoughts returned to Susan. She was in good hands with Sarah and her family. This temporary situation was contingent upon her acquiring her place. Sarah, our beautiful and sweet sister from Greenville married in 1958. Sarah and Susan were the best sisters in the world. I had suspected that Susan's tenure living with us was short term. I knew that she'd have issues and problems dealing with Mitch.

"Help me get my suitcase and clothes loaded," Susan requested.

"I will Susan. Why don't you wait and leave after lunch?"

"No, David Lee, I'd better get on down the road."

"Susan, I promise that I'll look after Mother and Ronnie."

"I know that you will. Be a man and remember what I told you."

"Susan, I will. And I'll pray every night for things to improve."

Ronnie and I loaded Susan's suitcases and belongings. Shortly afterward, she was ready to depart. Mother left for work earlier and had already bid her farewell. Mitch returned from working the graveyard shift and went to bed. There was no reason to prolong it anymore. The stark reality of the matter was that she was leaving.

"Come here, you guys, and kiss me. Y'all take care of Mother."

We stood in the front yard and waved goodbye as she boarded her car and backed down the driveway. She waved and blew kisses as she departed.

Ronnie returned to bed and caught up on his sleep. He had experienced a trying day as he worked in the garden and swam at the Redwood swimming pool.

I entered our home and discovered that Mitch had left me a worklist on the dining room table. I sat down at the table and picked up the list and investigated. I wanted to go to baseball practice at 2:30 pm, so I got busy.

The worklist read as follows:

1. Be quiet and don't wake me up, unless it's an emergency.
2. Shell the bag of purple-hull peas that's in the dining room corner.
3. Water and feed the dogs and clean their cages.
4. Sweep the driveway and the front and back steps.
5. Turn on the sprinkler for forty-five minutes in the front yard and then relocate the water hose to the backyard and water it for about forty-five minutes. Roll up the hose the way you found it when you finish.
6. Don't leave the house until you complete your work.

After I surveyed the work list, I grabbed a large bowl and a sack of peas and began the task at hand. However, thoughts about Susan and Marilyn Monroe dominated by thoughts. Two dynamic blondes vacated my life on the same day. What was the probability of that happening to someone?

CHAPTER 12
EXTRA BASES

I got busy with my work assignments. Billy was to meet me at 1:00 pm and we planned to ride the city bus to the ball fields at Vicksburg City Park. I paced myself and completed every chore on my work list. I prepared a tomato and cheese sandwich with potato chips and milk for Ronnie and myself.

"Ronnie, I'm leaving shortly, but don't make loud noises because Mitch is asleep. Don't bring any neighborhood kids into the house."

Ronnie told me to save my breath because he wasn't going to stay at home. He'd decided to play with Mickey McGinnis. The McGinnis family was friendly and lived two doors down. I saw Billy as he approached.

Ronnie followed me outside and asked, "Can I borrow your Monopoly game?"

"Yes, but don't lose any game pieces or play money. Make sure that everything is counted and returned to its correct slot."

"I'll take care of it and won't lose any of the pieces."

"Be careful and do what I told you."

Ronnie winked and replied, "I never have and never will. See you later, David Lee".

I chased him a few steps, and he ran back into the house and retrieved the monopoly game. I went inside and grabbed my baseball glove and departed for baseball practice.

We waited for the Drummond Street bus on the corner of Sky Farm Avenue. The city bus was to arrive in a few minutes. Before it arrived, we practiced every pitch that we knew. Billy taught me how to throw a two and three finger knuckleball. In my mind, I mastered the fastball and curve. Like clockwork, the bus arrived on time. The bus driver was an elderly gentleman named Mr. Jackson. His grandchildren attended the same junior high school as me. He was a friendly man who played with the children and joked with them.

Visions of baseball greats were on my mind as the bus churned, and bumped through the streets of Vicksburg. Of course, my favorite players were Mickey Mantle and Roger Maris of the New York Yankees. Last year, 1961 was a stellar year for Mickey and especially Roger. They had a home run competition all year. Roger hit sixty-one homers, and Mickey wasn't far behind with fifty-four. Roger set a major league record and eclipsed Babe Ruth's record of sixty homers in a season. The sportswriters pointed out that the Babe had accomplished this feat in fewer games. However, I patterned my hitting style and stance after Rocky Colavito of the Detroit Tigers and formerly of the Cleveland Indians. I loved his aggressive style at the plate. He challenged and pointed the tip of his bat at the pitcher in between pitches. It was like he intended to knock the ball down their throats.

I was a baseball card collector and had been since 1957. I religiously stashed them in a shoebox that was in my closet. I divided the baseball cards by rubber bands into separate teams. Also, I kept them separated by National and American League ball clubs. I met with neighborhood card collectors and traded cards. Many nickels and dimes were in the purchase of these hundreds of baseball cards. For this reason, there were duplicates of the same players. These were the ones that you traded to receive cards that you needed. Baseball cards, in their colorful packages, included a piece of delicious gum. We chewed the gum with nervous excitement as we shuffled through our newly purchased cards and anticipated a discovery of one of our favorite baseball stars.

The Second All-Star Major League Baseball Game was right around the corner. I favored the American League over the National League. However, I cheered for some National League Players like "Stan the Man" Musial of the St. Louis Cardinals and Lew Burdette, Warren Spahn, Eddie Mathews, and Hank Aaron of the Milwaukee Braves. Unfortunately, the American League had been dominated by the National League for the past few years. In fact, the first All-Star Game this summer was won by the National League 3 to 1. I watched the game on TV from Washington D.C., and President John F. Kennedy threw out the first pitch. Maury Wills of the Los Angeles Dodgers, the fastest man in baseball, was the MVP of the first All-Star game. Roberto Clemente of the Pittsburgh Pirates and Willie Mays of the San Francisco Giants were outstanding. I hoped that in a couple of weeks, the American League would win the second game.

We traveled by the manicured lawns, beautiful trees, plants and flowers, and impressive historical homes. The scenery filled me with pride in being a part of the beautiful City of Vicksburg. We moved to Vicksburg from Greenville two years ago, and I loved the people and uniqueness of the city.

At baseball practice, Billy was outstanding. He hit three towering homers. I hit a few hard grounders, and line drives to the outfield. We prepared for a baseball game on Friday. Afterwards, we planned a campout on Mole Hill which was a block east of my house.

The week progressed slowly, but surely, without any controversy or hitches. Susan called during the week and informed us that she was fine and had obtained a new job. Ronnie, always glued to the TV set, began playing outside with friends. Mother fell into her routine; she worked out of town a few days a week and worked out of her office when in town. Mitch worked the graveyard shift but was disgruntled with this job schedule. He threatened to quit ICRR if he didn't receive day shift work.

We won the Friday baseball game by a score of 9 to 6. We played seven innings of solid baseball. Billy hit a homer over the centerfield fence and delighted the home crowd. Also, he doubled and went two for four for the game. His defense was excellent, and runners didn't dare challenge his rifle arm. I went one for three with a walk and a single. I batted in one run and scored another. Coach Childs put me in as a relief pitcher in the fifth inning. I retired the first three batters that I faced and allowed one hit. One batter flew out, one grounded out, and I struck out the other. It was funny because I set the next one up as I threw two fastball strikes. He dug in and anticipated another fastball. However, when I threw a slow, two-finger knuckleball, he tried to hold up, but lost his balance and fell as he swung. Coach Childs was proud of the way that we played, and the team relished the win.

We returned home satisfied by the victory and anticipated the upcoming campout.

CHAPTER 13
DANCING ON THE COALS

After the game, I arrived home at 5:00 pm, took a bath, and within ten-minutes departed. Mother said that she wanted a conversation with me before I left. I brushed my teeth and hair and went into the living room to meet Mother.

"Mama, do you want to talk with me?"

"I want you to be careful on the campout tonight. Remember what happened to Donnie in 1952." She continued, "Donnie visited Grandmother on the Mississippi Gulf Coast, and he and three boys camped out. Donnie was nine years old. They built a campfire, and during the night it became chilly. Donnie inched close to the fire to capture its warmth. Also, he zipped his sleeping bag up all the way. During the early morning hours, one of the young boys revived the fire. He stirred the coals with a stick and added wood, but nothing happened. Then he doused the fire with gasoline, and it exploded. Donnie's sleeping bag was in flames from the explosion. He died in the ambulance on the way to the hospital."

Mother's hands shook, and she was ashen pale. She puffed on her Winston cigarette. I felt sorry for Mother because of her difficult life. I recalled the funeral, the flowers atop Donnie's grave, and the heartbreak that was shared by all and it was one of my earliest recollections.

I assured Mother that I was responsible and that there wasn't gasoline at the campout. I asked her not to worry.

Ronnie asked, "Mama, can I campout with David Lee?"

"No! I need you to help me run errands today. While we're downtown, I'll buy you a cone of Seale-Lily Ice Cream."

"Yes!"

I gathered a few items and supplies for the campout which included: backpack, sleeping bag, canteen, four coat hangers for (hot dogs and marsh mellows), a box of matches, and my trusted hunting knife and hatchet. The weatherman predicted clear and warm with no chance of rain. It was perfect weather, and I looked forward to an enjoyable, time. I bid my family farewell and headed for the infamous "Mole Hill."

I was the first one who arrived at the campsite. I prepared a few things before the others arrived. I cleared a good camping spot and removed weeds, bushes, and debris. Since it was a warm night, we decided to sleep in the open in sleeping bags. We watched out for what we called moles. They were centipedes that were prevalent on "Mole Hill."

Billy, Jimmy, and Joey approached the campsite with camping gear. Darkness fell, and we scurried and set up camp. I gathered sticks and wood for a fire and sought stones to make a border.

Soon, we ignited sticks and wood and had a fire. We encircled the campfire and unwound coat hangers and straightened them for cooking skewers. We passed out the weenies and cooked them until charred. We substituted sliced bread with hot dogs buns. The only condiment was mustard. We consumed two packages of hot dogs in a matter of minutes. Then, we passed out a large bag of marshmallows. Jimmy brought strawberry Kool-Aid in his canteen, and we shared the communal drink. We charred the marshmallows until they were melted, gooey, and sticky. Nonetheless, we gorged ourselves and ate the entire bag. After we devoured our assortment of morsels, we still had an ample supply of peanuts and pecans. The nuts were in two cans and available if we woke in the night with a case of hunger pangs.

Billy said, "Do you know what you need after a good meal?" He reached into his backpack and produced a handful of small sticks and showed them to us.

"Do y'all know what these are?"

"Are those grave vines?"

"Yes, these are grapevines, and we're going to smoke them."

Billy handed us grapevine cigarettes and passed a burning stick around for a light. We had seen our parents smoke after a meal and thought we'd try it. I lit a grapevine and inhaled too vigorously. Suddenly, a flame of fire rushed down my throat, and this wasn't my idea of a pleasurable activity. I threw my grapevine into the fire and quit on the spot. The others laughed as they smoked their grapevines. Jimmy exhaled and blew smoke rings after a few minutes.

After we finished our meal and smoking adventure, we arranged our sleeping bags on the outer perimeter of the fire. Full bellies and all we stargazed and identified different stars and constellations in the night sky. We located Venus, the North Star, and the Little and the Big Dipper.

Joey yelled out, "There!" as he pointed his index finger in the southwestern night sky. "That's 'The Awshurr.'"

Billy replied, "Wascally Wabbit. Joey, you couldn't find the Archer if he shot you in the butt with an arrow."

We laughed at the funny comment as we scanned the heavens in search of constellations. Suddenly, we observed a shower of shooting stars from the western sky. Also, as the night progressed, we recognized the Milky Way. We were amazed at the beauty of the stars and planets. The wind lazily blew in from the northwest and provided immediate relief to our perspired bodies.

As the night progressed, we sat on sleeping bags and told jokes. We started with the standard "knock-knock" jokes.

Joey started with "Knock-knock."

"Who's there?"

"Boo."

"Boo who?"

"Please, don't cry."

We laughed and complimented Joey for his joke-telling skills. We noted that he was an aspiring future comedian like a Red Skelton or Danny Kaye. We asked Jimmy if he had a "knock-knock joke." He indicated that he had indeed.

"Knock-knock"

"Who's there?"

"Madame"

"Madame who?"

"Open up! My damn foot's in the door."

We hysterically laughed because the joke was funny and racy. This joke contained a perfect combination of ingredients for boys our age.

We exhausted every "Knock-knock" joke that we recalled. We then moved on from standard to scary jokes. That was the typical script and sequence of events on a campout.

"I have a joke," I said.

I stood up and used my body to assist in the explanation of the joke.

"This one is called the 'Old Chinese Man and his Laundry.' Imagine an old Chinese man who worked inside a laundry business. A group of elementary school children was there on a field trip. He demonstrated how to wash and clean clothes the ancient Chinese way."

The old Chinese man said, "Children come in close in a semi-circle and sit around my wooden washtub and washboard. I'll show you how to wash clothes the ancient Chinese way. FIRST: "I take a towel, put the towel in water, and I add detergent. I go wishy-washy and wishy-washy and then I held it up. It looks good, feels good, and he sniffed it and said: The towel smells good too." Then, he folded the towel and put the towel in the stack."

SECOND: "I take the shirt, put the shirt in water, and I add detergent. I go wishy-washy and wishy-washy and then I hold up the shirt. The shirt looks good, feels good, and sniffed it and said: The shirt smells good too. Then, folded the shirt and put the shirt on the stack."

THIRD: "I take a big woman's panties, put panties in water, and add detergent. I go wishy-washy and wishy-washy and then I hold up the panties. The panties look good, feel good, and he sniffed and said, Oh No! The old

95

Chinese man dipped the panties back into the water and added a half a box of detergent and scrubbed and said, I go wishy-washy and wishy-washy."

Billy, Joey, and Jimmy rolled over on top of their sleeping bags doubled up in laughter. Jimmy, who had consumed quite a vast smorgasbord of hot dogs, pecans, peanuts, marshmallows, and strawberry Kool-Aid, let out a loud flutter blast!

We all yelled, "Scobey and Pokes!"

Jimmy tardily yelled, "Scobey!"

His response was too late by the rules of the game. We were obligated by the strict rules of the game to administer Jimmy a punch in the arm. I held back and didn't wallop him because I realized that chances were good that I'd suffer the same fate. We had all consumed high amounts of food.

It was the witching hour, and the flames and cinders flickered and hypnotically put us in a sleepy state. As the night air cooled, our eyelids became heavy, and Jimmy was the first one to call it a night and slipped into his sleeping bag. The rest of us stayed up late and told ghost stories. We covered the gamut of everything that was eerie, spooky, and macabre. Most of the ghost stories were about cemeteries, haunted houses, and dead Confederate soldiers. Also, we told a story about the Pennsylvania State Memorial Monument in the Vicksburg National Military Park. This monument had five bronze medallion faces of Pennsylvania Union Officers. The legend was that if you shone your headlights on their faces, that you saw bloody tears as they ran down their cheeks. Also, we told stories of the infamous "Hookman." Legend had it that when lovers parked in secluded areas that there was a possibility that they encountered the "Hookman." One night a couple of lovers made-out and the girl heard an eerie noise. She became spooked and demanded to leave. Her boyfriend thought that she was just silly and paranoid. However, he jumped up and started the car and sped away. They pulled into a gas station and checked the outside of his vehicle. He discovered a bloody hook hanging from the passenger side door.

I exhausted my repertoire of stories and tales. I covered all the evil characters of which I was familiar. Which included: "Dracula," "Wolf Man," "The Fly," "The Mummy," "Frankenstein," "Red Eye," "Godzilla," "The Creature from the Black-Lagoon," "The Blob," and the "Attack of the Crab Monsters." We even rehashed stories from the old episodes of '*The Twilight Zone*' and '*Shock Theater*.'"

At 1:00 am, we climbed into our sleeping bags, and it occurred to me that it was unwise that we told ghost stories. Well, it was too late now! My mind drifted from scary stories to thoughts about my family. I missed my sisters, mother, and brother and wondered if Mitch had behaved himself. I was lucky because I had a wonderful family and good friends. I always said prayers before I slept. Tonight, wasn't different from any other night.

I prayed, "Now I lay me down to sleep, I pray the Lord my soul to keep, and if I should die before I wake, I pray the Lord my soul to take." I added to my prayer, "Dear Lord, please bless my family and help me to become a better person. God, protect us and please keep us safe. I pray for this in your Holy and precious name Jesus Christ. AMEN."

I got up and checked the fire and gazed at the stars and slipped back into my sleeping bag, positioned my pillow, and within minutes fell asleep.

I woke by death curdling screams!

"What is it? What's going on?"

Joey and Billy jumped up out of their sleeping bags. Jimmy sat beside the fire and rubbed and blew on his feet. Evidently, like Ronnie, he was a sleepwalker. He had walked across the hot coals. After a few minutes, Jimmy went back to sleep as if nothing happened. We shook our heads in disbelief and agreed that ghost stories weren't on the agenda for our next campout. We agreed that we thought that we were attacked by an evil monster when we heard Jimmy's screams.

We woke at 5:30 am and broke camp. We rolled up our sleeping bags, packed our gear, and cleaned up the camping area.

Billy asked, "Would like to go the movie this afternoon?"

"Let me ask my parents first."

"I'll give you a call before 11:00 am to see if you can go. The movie that's showing is the *'Bird Man of Alcatraz'* with Burt Lancaster."

"Burt Lancaster! He's my favorite actor. My favorite movies are *Elmer Gantry* and *The Rose Tattoo.*"

"I didn't see those movies, but I heard that they were good."

"Those movies were great!"

We broke camp and went separate ways with intentions and hopes of getting together in the afternoon. I sneaked into my house. Thank God, Mother left the back door unlocked. Quietly, I placed my camping supplies in the proper places and put my dirty clothes in the clothes hamper. I went to my bedroom with the intention of much-needed sleep. Mother's bedroom door was closed, but I heard the song *"I Can't Stop Loving You"* by Ray Charles as it played. I crawled into bed, hugged the pillow, released a sigh of relief, and within minutes fell asleep.

CHAPTER 14
LET'S TWIST

After about an hour, I got up and bathed. Mother's radio still blasted out tunes. The song *"Running Scared"* by Roy Orbison played. I knocked on her door, but there wasn't a response. I checked for her car. Mother's car was in the driveway, but Mitch's Jeep was gone. I panicked because I thought something was wrong. I knocked on her bedroom door. My first thought was that Mother was hurt or even worse. Her door was unlocked so entered and feared the worst scenario!

Mother was in bed with her back to the door.

I whispered as I touched and shook her shoulder, "Mother, wake up, are you OK?"

"David Lee is that you?" Mother muttered as she reached over and turned off the radio.

"Yes, it's me."

"David Lee, shut my door so that we can talk."

Mother looked at me with a sad and distressed look. She shook her head back and forth and said, "We fought and argued most of the night. He returned from drinking and started yelling that I was spoiling you and Ronnie too much. He warned me if things didn't improve that he was going to leave. He threw things and acted crazy."

"He's not going anywhere. I wish that he would leave."

100

"I don't think that I can continue to live with a man who doesn't love or respect my children. Besides, I don't feel that he loves me anymore. I think that he loves only himself."

I almost jumped out of my skin when the bedroom door flew open. Ronnie ran toward Mother with arms outstretched. They embraced, and Mother caressed Ronnie's forehead and kissed him.

"That's my baby boy!" Mother exclaimed, "Good morning, did you sleep well last night?"

"No, Mother. I heard all that loud yelling, fussing, and fighting. Mitch was cursing and throwing things."

"I'm sorry that you heard that commotion."

There was a knock on the front door and were nervous. Our anxiety level was sky high. We thought that Mitch had returned. I went into the living room and peeped out of the side of the picture window. I recognized the familiar and friendly face of Mrs. Rosie. She saw me, waved, and then motioned for me to open the door.

"Good Morning, Mrs. Rosie."

"Well, good morning back to you. Where's Mrs. Evelyn?"

"She's in her bedroom. I was just talking to her. "

"Where's Mr. Mitch?"

"I don't know, and I don't care."

"David Lee, Mrs. Rosie said. You'd better watch your mouth because you're aware that Mr. Mitch doesn't play with children."

Mrs. Rosie walked to Mother's bedroom, and Ronnie went to the living room to watch "Tom and Jerry" cartoons. After about fifteen minutes, Mrs. Rosie returned to the living room.

Mrs. Rosie approached me and whispered, "Did you see your Mother's jaw?"

"No, I didn't notice!"

"You didn't see all that swelling on your Mother's face?"

"What? Mother's face shows swelling?"

Mrs. Rosie nodded her head up and down in affirmation.

After a few minutes, Mother emerged from the bathroom and asked, "Does anybody want biscuits and brown gravy? I know that's your favorite, David Lee."

"Ms. Evelyn, let me help you fix that."

Ronnie said, "I'd rather eat pancakes with syrup and butter."

"Mrs. Rosie, why don't you cook the pancakes and I'll fix the biscuits and gravy?"

"Let's get some life back into this house," Mother offered." Let's get some music going on the radio. Turn off that TV and let's dance."

"Ok! Ronnie responded. I've already seen this cartoon before anyway."

I tuned in to WQBC radio station, and a singer wailed, "Come on baby, let's do the twist." We yelled, "That's Chubby Checker!"

He sang the verse, "Around and around and around and around we go yeah! Up and down and all around we go yeah!"

We pulled back the rugs and planted ourselves onto the living room floor. In our stocking feet, we sang and danced like maniacs to the twist. It was great that we had life and fun back in our home again. Mother and Mrs. Rosie were special ladies. Also, I was delighted that Ronnie enjoyed himself. The next song that played was, *"Little Sister"* by Elvis Presley. I grabbed the broom and strummed it like a guitar. I sneered and puckered my lips and shook my skinny hips. I twisted and turned my left foot and leg like I extinguished a lit cigarette on the living room floor. Mother and Mrs. Rosie yelled, "Go, Elvis, Go."

Mother checked on the biscuits in the oven and made brown gravy. Mrs. Rosie said the black skillet was hot enough for pancakes.

"I'm hungry enough to eat biscuits and gravy, and pancakes smothered in syrup or molasses."

Everyone laughed at my silly comment, but the underlying and unspoken mood in our home was one of melancholy. I knew that Mother put on a brave front for Ronnie and me. Mrs. Rosie was right about the left side of Mother's face. I shook emotionally and went to the bathroom and held back tears. I was upset for my dear mother.

CHAPTER 15
BIRDMAN OF ALCATRAZ

The phone rang, and I yelled, "I got it! That has to be Billy."

It was Billy, and he asked if I'd checked with Mother about the movie.

"Not yet, but hold on, I'm asking now."

"Can I go to the movie with Billy this afternoon? He's leaving his house at 1:00 pm."

"You can go if you take Ronnie with you."

"No problem, Ronnie is welcome to go with us."

Ronnie asked, "Wait a minute, not so fast, what's playing?"

"The Bird Man of Alcatraz" starring Burt Lancaster. It's showing at the Joy Theater."

"No thanks; I'll wait for this one out. Maybe we can go and see the horror film 'A Bucket of Blood' at the Strand Theater later in the week."

"That sounds good to me. I love those scary movies too."

"What's that strong, overpowering smell?" Mother asked.

"That's me smelling good. I put on English Leather cologne that I got for my last birthday".

"That smells like rotten pickle juice. I'm going to stick with Old Spice."

"Yes, you can go. You guys have a good time at the movies."

"Thanks, Mother, we will."

"Billy, Mother said that I could go. I'll be at your house soon."

I worried about Mother because of the volatile situation that Mitch created. However, life continued, and any semblance of normalcy was good for our state of mind. I hoped that Mother and Ronnie ventured out and did something enjoyable.

"By the way, Mother, what are you and Ronnie going to do today?"

"We're going over to my friend Mabel Tillman's house and visit. If time allows, we'll drive around and enjoy the scenery. It'll be good to get out and relax."

"OK! I'll be back later this afternoon. I hope that y'all have a good day. Good-bye."

I arrived at Billy's house at 1:00 pm. We walked down the hill to Sky Farm Avenue and caught the downtown bus. We got off the bus at the corner of Crawford and Cherry Streets and made a mad dash to the Joy Theater. We made certain we arrived in time to view upcoming previews. After we paid admission, we went into a crowded lobby. We waited in the back doorway of the theater for a few minutes before we entered. Our eyes adjusted to the pitch black and we proceeded down the aisle.

The Joy Theater was magnificent; it consisted of three distinct sections for moviegoers. There was also a balcony for Colored people. The show was clean and had an ornate architectural design. There was a mean lady who worked there, who roamed up and down the aisles. She policed the movie with the aid of her trusty, glaring flashlight. She corrected talkers and rude individuals. We called her "Nancy Nazi," AKA, "The Enforcer." She probably weighed ninety-pounds soaking wet. Nonetheless, she planted fear in the souls of mischievous children.

We found seats in time and watched previews. Billy scoped out the place and noticed a couple of cute girls who sat in the middle section. I waited a few minutes before I sneaked a peep, so it wasn't too obvious. As soon as I turned around and looked, Billy waved at them, and they covered their mouths and giggled. Even though embarrassed, I noticed that they were cute. I hadn't seen them before and knew they weren't Vicksburg girls.

After about fifteen minutes, we went to the concession stand for refreshments. As we walked down the aisle, we glanced over at them. Billy smiled and winked at them. One of the girls smiled and waved. We bought refreshments and returned to our seats. We looked their way again, and they giggled and squirmed in their seats. Billy was a charmer, and there was no doubt that he exuded confidence.

The movie was great! It was about Robert Stroud who was in prison for life. He maintained his sanity as he tended birds at Alcatraz Prison. I thought this was a great lesson in life. Even in miserable times, you remained active and overcame obstacles. I reflected that personally, I maintained a sense of humor. Also, I refused to allow adverse situations to dictate who I was as a person.

After the movie, we met the two girls in front of the Joy Theater. They introduced themselves as Cindy and Sheila. They lived and attended school in the Culkin Community. Culkin located on the outskirts of Vicksburg. We exchanged names and phone numbers and left the movie theater full of confidence.

We walked a few blocks down Walnut Street and visited St. Paul's Catholic Church. We entered the church and offered a silent prayer. I lit a candle for Mother's safety and peace of mind. Then, we turned right on Clay Street and went to the YMCA where we intended to shoot a basketball and lift weights.

We'd spent our money at the Joy Theater except for return bus fare. For this reason, we sneaked into the YMCA which was a precarious proposition. Usually, one entered and ran past elderly Mr. Hadley Burns. However, this was dangerous because if he cornered you and called security you were in trouble. We climbed the stairs and went to the balcony that overlooked the gym. We saw a friend, and he swung the rope to us. I grabbed the rope and swung out three feet. My body spun while I held on and shimmied down the 40' rope. After I landed on the gym floor, I pulled the rope over to the side of the balcony for Billy.

"Man, it's high up here. A person could break his neck if he fell."

"I'll try and catch you in the event you fall."

Billy replied, "That's so funny that I forgot to laugh. Steady the rope because I'm going for it. Geronimo!"

Billy jumped and wrapped his hands and feet to the rope and shimmied down in a matter of seconds. However, inside the gym, we eluded Mr. Burns because he came into the gym often for a head count. We went straight to the weight room and lifted weights for forty-five minutes. Then, we went to the ball courtroom and played a game of handball. The rules of the game were that you hit the ball against the wall and if it bounced once you hit it with your hand. However; if the ball bounced twice, then you kicked the ball with your foot. Handball was like tennis in that you only received a point if you served. Even though Billy had a husky physique, he was an agile and skilled player. His movements were fluid and smooth, and he was quick and light on his feet. He won our game 21 to 11, and it wasn't as close as the score indicated.

We heard a rumor, from the other boys, that Mr. Burns was in pursuit of two young men who hadn't paid. We knew that we were the subjects of the search. We hid in the weight room under a wrestling mat. A young man accompanied Mr. Burns. We heard them as they talked from the safety of our stinky hideout. The young, rat fink said that one of them was dark skinned, husky, and had a muscular build. The other one was tanned, skinny, and smelled of strong cologne. We laughed as we made a mad dash out of the YMCA gym right past our pursuers. In my flight, I left an overpowering and intoxicating trail of aroma behind for the gym rats.

Mr. Burns yelled. "Y'all stop! Come back and pay me your admission."

Billy replied, "Sorry. You can't get blood out of a turnip. We're broke, and we'll have to pay you the next time that we see you."

"Make sure that you do! I'll remember that you whippersnappers owe me money. You two can't return to the YMCA until you've paid up in full."

"Yes, sir, Mr. Burns, we'll pay you back. Have a beautiful day!" I responded.

After we left the YMCA, we climbed the hill at Clay Street and headed for the Cherry Street bus stop. We passed a hot tamales cart at the top of the hill, and our stomachs growled.

An older Colored gentleman pushed a tamale cart while he sang, "Get your hot and tasty tamales. Mister Solly makes them. A dozen costs a half a dolly. After you eat them, you're going to yell 'Good Golly, Miss Molly.'"

We let out a big laugh of approval. "The man is a great poet," I said.

"Are you giving away any free samples?" Billy asked.

"No Sir," he announced. "I know that you two scholars have a little pocket change or jingle jangle in your pockets."

"How much would it be for four?" Billy asked.

"I only sell them by the dozen. Tamales cost .50 cents a dozen," the man replied. "That's the best deal in town."

Besides our bus fare, we had two nickels and two pennies between us.

We told the gentleman that they smelled delicious, but we'd better not buy any.

The reality was that if we purchased hot tamales, we'd have to walk home.

Since we were both exhausted from the day's activities, we fought off our hunger pangs. We inhaled the aroma of the world's most delicious smelling hot tamales as we waited for the bus. The bus arrived after fifteen minutes, and we headed home.

Fortunately, as we returned to Billy's house, I was invited to eat with his family. Mrs. Nancy Jo served the vegetable stew, ham sandwiches, and sweet tea. There was something special about a home-cooked meal when you were hungry. I had an insatiable appetite fueled by an image of spicy tamales. Two bowls of stew, two ham sandwiches, a snicker bar, and two glasses of sweet tea sated my appetite. I consumed a large volume of food. My stomach protruded out, and my body resembled a giant marshmallow (my stomach) with two toothpicks (my legs). If I consumed this amount of food on a regular basis, I'd have a full-figure. Consequently, instead of skinny jokes, then, then I'd be the recipient of fat jokes. Sometimes in life, it seemed that you just couldn't win!

CHAPTER 16
THE DIE IS CAST

I consumed the hearty, but delicious meal, thanked Mrs. Nancy Jo and headed home. My prevailing thought was that Mitch was home. I departed, and every step was in a robotic, calculated manner. I took a deep breath and thrust my body with momentum and scaled the steepest part of the hill. I peered to my right and viewed the cul-de-sac where Mitch always parked his Jeep.

There it was! His Jeep parked in his usual spot. All optimism left, and my heart sunk to the nadir of disappointment.

I inhaled a deep breath of warm evening air and opened the front door and entered quietly. I heard loud yells that came from Mother's bedroom. Ronnie hovered in front of the TV and watched *"The Lucy Show."* He noticed that I'd entered and jumped to his feet and embraced me tightly. His eyes were filled with tears as he hugged me. Strangely, his body shook and jerked in a rhythmic pattern that resembled an electrical shock. I felt sorry for my brother and realized that he was an emotional wreck.

I knew that Ronnie was nervous and devastated. I invited him to join me on the front steps for conversation. Mosquitoes, June bugs, and an occasional moth swarmed around our front porch light. It was humid and sultry, and perspiration poured down our brows, necks, and backs.

"Ronnie, everything is going to be alright. I promise you that."

Tears raced down Ronnie's face. He was distraught. I embraced him again and tried to soothe his feelings and calm him down. Ronnie choked on tears

111

as he spoke. He released incoherent sounds from deep inside his soul. It was clear that these emotions were pent up for a long time.

I embraced him again and stated. "Ronnie let it all out, and you'll feel better."

After about twenty-minutes, Ronnie stopped crying and we reentered the house. The attic fan was always noisy but was extra loud tonight. It competed with the noise of the strong argument that came from Mother's bedroom. Ronnie had a headache; I gave him aspirin, a glass of water, and a wet cloth to put on his forehead. He headed to the safety of his bedroom and pitifully looked back as he entered his room. I heard as he pushed in his doorknob and locked it. I returned to the living room and sat down on the couch.

Mitch yelled, "Evelyn, your boys are bad, and they need their asses whipped." He continued, "Ronnie, with his nervous little ass, is going to be a queer if you don't stop spoiling and coddling him. David Lee pisses me off with his smartass attitude."

Mother replied, "My boys are good kids, and they're always trying to please you. You don't give them a chance. Why are you attacking them? They're children of ten and thirteen years of age."

"You and your snotty nose kids can kiss my ass," Mitch growled. "I'm sick of this arrangement."

Mitch slammed the bedroom door and stormed down the hallway. I heard his loud, and intimidating footsteps headed my way. When he noticed that I was on the couch, he went ballistic! His eyes bulged and glared, and his face turned red. He stood over me in an intimidating manner. He unbuckled his belt and slowly pulled it from his belt loops. He doubled up his belt and attacked. He struck me with forceful lashes.

He yelled to Mother, "Here's your son, David Lee. He's finally come home and is in here eavesdropping." He said, "I'll teach you who's the boss you little bastard."

I held my arms in a defensive position and protected my head and face. I backed out of the living room and headed toward my bedroom as Mitch continued the beating. I knew that he wanted to hurt me. Mother met us and yelled for him to quit hitting me. She grabbed his arm and pleaded for him to stop.

"You've already whipped him, Mitch. You've made your point, and now you need to stop!"

He shoved Mother against the wall like he was possessed and threw his belt down on the floor. Then, he slapped me in my face. Mother tripped and fell. I grabbed him and pushed him back to protect Mother. Mitch was angered, and he hit me with his fist. I fell back onto my bedroom floor. He continued the onslaught and punched me in the face as I arose. The force of the hit pushed me backward and propelled me against my bedroom window. My left elbow went through my windowpane. My blinds fell and collapsed on top of me. Then, with his left hand, he grasped the front of my shirt and pulled me toward him. I smelled the robust and putrid odor of underarm perspiration and whiskey. He pulled on my shirt and jerked me around in his drunken rage. He pinned me in the hallway and was on top of me and slapped and choked me. Mother pulled on his arm, but he pushed her back. I struggled to loosen his strong grasp. I was scared and feared the outcome. I struggled to breathe with his heavy weight on top of me.

At the same time, Ronnie opened his door and yelled, "Leave my brother alone. He hasn't done anything to you. "You're a big bully."

"You shut up and get your little ass back in your room, or you'll get whipped too!" Mitch shouted.

I remembered what Susan told me. The only alternative I had was to fight back. I reached back with all my strength and hit him on the side of the head. Mitch loosened his stronghold and staggered back in disbelief. He glared at me and was in the shock that I'd fought back. Mitch told Mother, "If he hits me, then he must think that he's a man. Tonight, I'm going to make a man out of your boy!" The attack continued.

Mother was overcome with emotion and fainted in the hallway. The physical assault continued, and I was exhausted and at his mercy. Luckily, after a few minutes, he loosened his grip and returned to his bedroom. I was sprawled out in the hallway. Mother recovered from fainting and asked me if I was hurt.

"Do you need for me to take you to the hospital?" She asked.

I shook my head from side to side and indicated "no."

Mother yelled at Mitch, "You're a sorry excuse for a man! What kind of man beats up a thirteen-year-old boy?"

There wasn't a reply. Mother and Ronnie consoled and comforted me. After a few minutes, I arose and went to the bathroom. I looked in the mirror and saw that my nose bled and my face was puffy. My ears rang like an alarm clock went off in my head. Also, my arms, back, and legs ached. My rib cage felt crushed. I was in pain when I took deep breaths. I experienced a sensation of shortness of breath and gasped for air. I drew bathwater and cleaned up and soaked my aching body. In the tub, I broke down and cried because I was manhandled and humiliated. I prayed to God to please help me and deliver me from this horrible situation. I knew that the "Die was Cast" because Mitch wouldn't forgive me for fighting back and I'd never forgiven him for shoving Mother.

After I bathed, I went to Ronnie's bedroom and checked on Ronnie and Mother. They were asleep, and I kissed them good night. Next, I went into the kitchen and drank a glass of water. My parched mouth, because of the excitement, tasted like I'd eaten cotton balls. As I finished my glass of water, I glanced at the calendar and noticed that tomorrow was Sunday, August 19. We only had a couple of weeks before we returned to school.

As I ventured down the hallway, Mitch snored like a grizzly bear over the sound of the attic fan. I went to bed that night with the realization that like Julius Caesar, I crossed the Rubicon, and there was no turning back. I feared what might happen to me and what tomorrow would bring.

CHAPTER 17
THE GREY GHOST

When I woke the next morning, I was greeted by sounds of nature. Birds chirped, and there were faint barks of distant dogs. My room was bright because the sun shone through my bedroom window. My window blinds were sprawled haphazardly across my bedroom floor. I noticed a few of my items strewn over my room. Sadly, he destroyed two of my most prized possessions from last night's incident. Mickey Mantle and Roger Maris New York Yankees Action figures were broken and beyond repair. The statuettes depicted my heroes posed in batting stances. They proudly donned their splendid New York Yankees pinstripe baseball uniforms.

My head and body ached as if hit by a train. I carefully peeled my bed covers away from my sore body. I winced from the pain from my face and back. Then, I went to the bathroom and washed my face and brushed my teeth. Mother was in the hallway when I exited the bathroom.

She nervously whispered, "Why don't you leave the house this morning until things cool down?"

"Are you sure, Mother?" I replied

"Yes! Here's $3.00. Just return later in the afternoon after I've had time to talk with Mitch about what happened last night." Mother hugged, and kissed me and told me to hurry.

I dressed and hoped that Billy had returned home from his paper route. As I descended the hill to his house, I saw his bicycle was in the carport. Unfortunately, it appeared that everyone was asleep. I borrowed Joey's football that was left in their front yard and meandered down the street toward the Methodist Church on Sky Farm Avenue. On the church's grassy lot, I practiced punting, kick-off, and field goals. However, my body was sore, so I stopped. Then, I threw the football to myself. I tossed the ball high into the air and ran to the predicted spot where it descended and caught it. For about an hour, I played this monotonous game. Next, I walked the neighborhood to occupy my time. Ultimately, I snuck back home to retrieve my bicycle. I climbed the hill on Ridgeway Street and entered my yard without detection. I grabbed my red Mercury bicycle and sped off like the wind. I flew down the hill, sore body and all, and welcomed the dangerous feat with an adrenaline rush.

I sought the refuge of Cedar Hill Cemetery as my next destination. The serenity of the cemetery always provided me a safe-haven. The gravesites were loyal and proven friends. The rolling hills, trees, plants, and flowers always provided me a sense of contentment. While I visited, I cleaned some of the tombstones and restored flowers back to their proper vases. I always took precautions and never walked on the gravesites. Strange as it seemed, I always loved these souls and cherished and respected their memories.

I crossed the Confederate Soldier's Rest portion of the cemetery and headed for a huge hackberry tree on a nearby hill. This location gave me a distinct and open view of my home. I positioned myself underneath the enormity of the hackberry tree. There were magnificent live oaks, fragrant magnolias, and tall cedar trees all around. In this setting, I laid down on the ground and rested. I used the football as a pillow and observed beautiful fluffy clouds overhead. They drifted overhead and complemented the azure-blue-morning sky. Hypnotically, the sun peeped out and greeted me from the gaps in the clouds. Nature played a game of peek-a-boo with me.

I was at peace with myself even though the night before was a hell on earth. Nothing mattered at this moment in time. I felt God's embrace, protection, and warmth. I felt a catharsis of my soul, and a new found and renewed spirit and sense of self-worth. No matter what misfortunes that I had experienced lately, the good things outweighed the bad. The blessings I had were a loving Mother, two great sisters, and a smart and talented brother. Also, I had great friends and lived in a beautiful and friendly city.

These thoughts went through my mind in conjunction with the peaceful warmth that I felt. I drifted off into a deep and peaceful slumber. I roused by the sound of running water and the deep voices of men in loud conversation. I yawned while I stretched my arms and legs. I gathered my thoughts and stood up and removed the grass and small sticks from my hair and clothes.

"Lord Jesus! Blessed Jesus! Sweet Jesus! Help us!" Somebody shouted.

I turned around and saw two elderly Colored gentlemen who stared at me as if I was a ghost.

I said, "Good morning. How are y'all doing?"

They carefully investigated me as they swayed back and forth in a crouched and deliberate inquisitive fashion.

"Why in God's green acre are you asleep in here with all these dead folks? Up here in this cemetery," one of the men asked.

"Don't you have a home?" The other man said.

"Yes, I have a home, but I just come in here and visit the residents of the cemetery sometimes. I'm not scared of the dead folks. It's the live folks, which I'm afraid because they're the ones that'll harm you," I explained.

They both let out a roar of laughter and slapped their knees and danced around in a euphoric dance of approval in response to what I'd said.

"Young man you're a strange little, skinny, White boy. You sleep in cemeteries and talk with the wisdom of a man-child. Also, you don't seem to mind that we're Colored folks, don't talk down to people, and you're mannerly."

While they talked, I mounted my bicycle and loaded the football in the basket and pushed off for momentum to get started. I waved goodbye to the gentlemen and said, "Have a great day."

As I departed, one of the men said, "John, when you first saw that White boy you thought that he was a ghost and you turned paler than him."

The other man replied, "You're the one. You'd need to check your pants because I think you made a large deposit, even though the bank closed on Sunday."

They laughed and poked fun at each other as I rode away toward Billy's house. I thought to myself, that in this big, beautiful, wonderful world that life was what you made it. You accepted the good with the bad. Most people had good intentions. I refused to allow negative things or people in my life to influence and dictate my future. I had dreams and goals and aspired for success and happiness. I planned to live every day one day at a time and hoped for the best.

CHAPTER 18
SAINTS AND SINNERS

After I left the cemetery, I returned to Billy's house and hoped to attend afternoon Mass with him. When I arrived, Joey and Jimmy sat on the front porch steps.

"Did you guys miss this?" I asked as I threw them their football.

"Wow! That was a Bart Starr type pass." I boasted.

"More like Belle Starr," Jimmy stated as he let his wrist go limp and walked around with his rear end grossly protruded.

I retaliated as I picked bagworms off one of their evergreen trees. After I gathered about seven or eight bagworms, I chased Jimmy and bombarded him in a blitzkrieg type-attack. Jimmy picked bagworms and counter-attacked my initial offensive. Joey joined in the bagworm battle. After the dust settled, there were worm-like cocoons that moved in a caterpillar fashion all over the yard. Of course, the next course of action was that we stepped on them and pulverized them into a squishy mess. The winner was the person who has the highest worm body count. We picked up all the bagworm casualties and placed them in a trash can. Their father was serious-minded and wouldn't tolerate scores of dead bagworms that littered his yard, front steps, and driveway.

As we completed our task at hand, Billy came out of his house.

He asked, "David Lee, would you like to go to St. Mary's Catholic Church with me?"

"Sure," I said. "That's precisely the reason that I'm here. I'm a little concerned because I've never attended Mass at St. Mary's Catholic Church."

"The parishioners there are friendly, and you'll enjoy the Mass," Billy replied.

"Billy before we go to Mass, can I use your telephone to call Mother?" I asked.

"Sure, but hurry because Daddy is going to drop us off at St. Mary's Church shortly. We won't be able to give you a ride home because we're going to visit my aunt after Mass."

"No problem," I replied. I'll call Jack since he lives in that area and find out if I can visit with him. I haven't seen him all summer."

I called Jack first, and he agreed to pick me up on his *Cruise Air* motorcycle. Also, he invited me to spend the night. He suggested that we meet down the hill from St. Mary's Catholic Church at Wilson's Grocery Store. Ryland was a friend whose uncle owned Wilson's. Next, I talked with Mother, and she approved my afternoon plans. I left Billy's house and jumped into his dad's work van. We drove away as I shut the door.

St. Mary's was a good experience for me. The congregation was courteous, and we felt at ease. We sat in the back row and participated in the Sacraments and received Communion. We had dark tans, but Billy was extremely dark. A few of the parishioners asked us if we were mixed. The Church was a beautiful structure, and we enjoyed a positive experience.

After Mass, I left Billy at the Church and headed to Wilson's Grocery Store. There were six Colored boys in front of the store when I arrived. They talked and milled around. Jack wasn't there yet, so I entered the store and spoke with Ryland. We had a good conversation and caught up on the news. Ryland was Chinese and was originally from Toronto, Ontario in Canada. He was an excellent student who made the honor roll. Ryland was athletic and kept himself in top physical shape. He consistently wore short-sleeve shirts which revealed his muscular arms. He dressed well and always had plenty of spending money.

I glanced out the front door and checked for Jack's arrival. Evidently, one of the Colored boys, became offended and thought that I stared at him. He pointed at me and mumbled something. I discounted this because I hadn't addressed him. After about ten or fifteen minutes, Jack entered the store, and we enjoyed a good visit. We had a conversation about the great summer. We agreed that we'd enjoyed the break from school. Jack and Ryland had started a project about a month ago. They purchased about twenty-pigeons and built a large walk-in pigeon cage behind Jack's house. Ryland planned to take the birds to Fort Hill, at 5:00 am in the morning, and let them fly back to their coops. I thought this was a great idea!

As we departed Wilson's Grocery Store, the tall Colored boy stood in front of the right screen door. He blocked our way and prevented us from exiting the store. It hadn't registered to me as to his intentions. I stepped to the other side and walked out the left side screen door. Jack and Ryland followed me.

As I exited the door, the Colored boy said, "Hey! Peckerwood, you'd better be scared."

The rest of his group surrounded me, and he stood directly in front of me. The young man danced around like heavyweight boxer Floyd Patterson which was intended to intimidate me. I looked at him in disbelief. It was stupid that he was bothering me.

"Did you hear what I said peckerwood? Are you scared?" He repeated. His friends laughed and agreed that I looked scared.

I blurted out, "No, I'm not scared of anyone."

I noticed that Jack had straddled his *Cruise-Air* motorcycle and had cranked it.

Ryland, who knew these guys, attempted to convince them to leave me alone. They told Ryland to stay out of it because it was none of his business. Then, the tall boy danced around in front of me and reached over with his left hand and slapped me. I went after him. I pushed him back against the storefront doorway area. He connected with a punch that busted my lip. As we continued to fight, I connected with a solid punch to his chin. He landed inside a trash can, located in the front of the store. All hell broke loose as everyone became agitated. His friends were angry and went into a verbal rage and hurled profane and threatening remarks at me.

Jack yelled, "Get on the back of the motorcycle and hurry." Ryland stood between me and the others with arms spread out and pleaded for me to leave. I jumped on the back of the motorcycle, and Jack gunned the motor as we climbed the steep hill.

The angry boys chased after us. They hurled bottles, sticks, rocks, and insults at us. However, by God's good grace, we escaped this ugly confrontation.

Jack pulled over to the side of the road after we had distanced ourselves from the angry crowd. He looked at me in utter shock and disbelief.

Jack asked, "What in the hell did you do to make those boys so angry?"

"Nothing, I replied. I think that the first guy was trying to show off in front of his friends at my expense. Maybe, because I'm skinny, he thought that I was weak."

Jack said, "I didn't know that you could fight. You knocked him in the trash can. I bet that he won't try and pick on you again."

I replied, "The sad part is that I just left a church, and you know that the minister wouldn't approve of fighting on the Sabbath."

CHAPTER 19
FLEW THE COOP

Jack was a unique person. He was highly intelligent and explored avenues in which most people were reluctant to venture. Jack was tall, red-headed, blue-eyed, with a pear-shaped body and big thighs. He dressed for comfort and preferred a terrycloth type shirt with a thin fabric for pants. To my knowledge, he never wore shorts or jeans.

Jack's house was an attractive two-story white antebellum home that was on the corner of Adams and Jackson Street. The location was a block from the Old Court House Museum. His father was a chiropractor who had a clinic in their home. They moved from Sacramento, California to Vicksburg about a year ago. Jack had three brothers, and the family was of Greek and Irish heritage. I dined with them occasionally, and their meals consisted of white grape juice, grape leaves, Greek moussaka, Greek salad, pita bread with hummus, and baklava for dessert.

We entered the back of their house, which was an enclosed patio. There were cages of parakeets, lovebirds, mynah birds, and even a grouchy macaw. They chattered as they flitted around in their cages. Jack put his cheek up against the bird's cage. Invariably, either a yellow, blue, or green parakeet pecked or kissed his cheek. The mynah bird performed as it gawked "Pretty boy." I stayed away from the macaw because it was territorial and didn't want to be bothered by our silly antics. Furthermore, it pecked if you infringed upon its space.

The adjoining room contained an item that was every young boy's dream it was a full-size, high-quality pool-table. On the wall was a pool wall-rack that had eight pool sticks on both sides. Openly stored and in abundance were balls, chalk, racks, and pool cue extenders. On the other end of the room, the score was kept by a string of beads. Strangely in the middle of the room and directly over the pool table was a beautiful chandelier. Also, downstairs there was a parlor, kitchen, bathroom, and an area that was an examination room for chiropractic patients. As one proceeded upstairs, by way of a beautiful winding staircase, there were bedrooms and bathrooms. In the front of the house, there was a large open porch, rocking chairs, and an exterior couch with side tables. In the back of their home, was a driveway that led to a one-bedroom apartment with parking areas. Next to the apartment, was Jack and Ryland's prize pigeon coop. They constructed the coop in the Spring and early part of Summer. The pigeon coop was built well and structurally sound. Jack and Ryland were excellent carpenters.

After we settled in Jack's house and greeted his family, we pursued other endeavors. His home was in a central location and was close to the downtown area and stores and shops.

"Do you want to go to a malt shop?" Jack inquired.

"Sure," I responded. "Where are we going?" I asked.

"Jerry's mother opened a small malt shop and restaurant on Openwood Street," Jack said.

The malt shop was less than a block from Jack's house. As we entered the establishment, we noticed that it was small with modest furnishings. There were booths on each side and several small tables with an assortment of chairs and stools. In the left corner was a counter where customers placed and picked up orders. Behind this area was a small kitchen and grill. There was a restroom in the right corner which was near a beautiful vintage 1950's Wurlitzer jukebox. The jukebox glowed with brown, gold, purple, and green fluorescent lights. The lights flashed in the area where you selected your songs. The song *"Duke of Earl"* by Gene Chandler blared and reverberated throughout the malt shop. We seated ourselves at a booth that had pictures of Bridgette Bardot and Sophia Loren posing provocatively. I noticed that there were celebrities' images over every booth.

Jerry ran up and greeted us. It was awesome that his family's business was a success. Jerry was a running back on the junior high football team. Also, he was a sprinter on the track team.

"Welcome to our malt shop," Jerry proudly announced. "Are you guys going to eat with us today?" He asked.

"Yes indeed," was our response.

"I recommend the hamburger basket," Jerry said. "Just go up to the counter and order from my mother, and she'll treat you right."

"OK. That sounds like a great plan," I stated.

As we ordered, there were four girls seated in a booth. On the opposite side of the room, there were several boys. We received our order numbers and returned to our seats. We dared each other, by way of a challenge, as to what brave soul asked a girl to dance first. I built up my nerve and was about to make a move. However, a song by The Shirelles played, *"Will You Love Me Tomorrow."* There was no way that I'd ask a girl to slow dance because I'd get laughed out of the malt shop.

I made my move when the *"Peppermint Twist"* played! I approached a young lady and asked, "Would like you to dance?"

"No thanks," she said.

I felt rejected and embarrassed from the refusal. I saved face and went to the restroom and played off the rejection while I gathered my thoughts. It was inevitable that verbal teasing from my friends would ensue. I told myself that at least I tried. Nothing ventured, nothing gained was my thought as I exited the restroom. However, a strange thing happened that made my day.

One of the young girls, who was with the "Queen of Rejection," asked me to dance. It was unbelievable! I went from" zero to hero "in less than a minute. I danced in my patented, unbridled, wild fashion which would've made "Joey Dee and the Starliters" proud. I twisted around and around and up and down until I gasped for air. I thanked the young lady and triumphantly returned to the boy's side of the restaurant. My friends hailed me as a hero. After I broke the ice with the first dance, the other guys swarmed the dance floor. We enjoyed an afternoon of great food, great music, and great conversation. I noticed that the young lady who refused my dance request attempted to get out of her seat. I observed that her legs were in braces. She struggled as she retrieved one of her crutches. It was obvious why she had rejected my offer to dance. The song the *Peppermint Twist* was too physically challenging for her. I hoped that I hadn't hurt her feelings.

I asked her, "Before you leave would you please slow dance with me?"

She looked at me with a beautiful smile and replied, "I'd love to dance with you." The next slow song played, and she braced herself with her left crutch, and we danced to "*Never My Love.*" A negative ended up positive.

When we returned to Jack's house, we played with tops. Jack had an old shoebox full. I chose a dusty blue bulky one with a long cord of string. We had a few practice spins, and then the competition commenced. The object was that your top would spin for the longest time, but was complicated because others tried to bump you out of the game. We had seven or eight of Jack's neighbors who participated. A group of younger kids struggled to keep their tops on the porch. For this reason, some of them yielded and became spectators. One of the neighborhood boys had a large mason jar full of lightning bugs. They blinked on and off in rapid succession. I looked in the jar and counted thirty-lightning bugs. Jack grabbed a handful of lightning bugs and smeared their bodies on the sides and hoods of parked cars. Amazingly, they glowed in a fluorescent greenish aqua color for a few seconds.

After about an hour of play and activity, mosquitoes feasted on our sweaty arms, necks, and legs. We returned inside and resumed playing monopoly, and card games like spades, hearts, and blackjack. Jack and two of his brothers were tired and went to bed. I went to the bathroom and urinated as a safety precaution. However, I hadn't experienced an accident in months and felt the issue had passed. I was devastated if anyone discovered that I had this problem at my age. Also, I was embarrassed about the abuses in our family. I was an honest person who lived under a cloak of secrecy.

As I bedded down for the night, I prayed and felt the excitement of the prospects of releasing pigeons on Fort Hill. I thought about Mother and how much I missed her. I hoped that she and Ronnie were safe. After a few minutes, I fell asleep. Jack woke me at 5:00 am. We dressed, like thieves in the night, and greeted the early morning.

As we arrived at the Pigeon coop, we saw Ryland as he gathered three of his birds to carry to Fort Hill and release. Jack followed suit and placed his in the same carrier cage. I transported the pigeons on the back of Jack's *Cruise-Air*. Ryland followed close behind us in his 1960 *Cushman Eagle.*

129

We departed into the darkness of Cherry Street and headed north toward the Vicksburg National Military Park. The morning air had a tinge of dampness. We rolled up and down the scenic hills of Vicksburg. I felt rejuvenated, refreshed, and excited as we traveled to reach our destination. As we approached the base of Fort Hill, I decided to walk up the hill. I felt awkward as I held a carrier cage full of pigeons from the back of to the *Cruise-Air*. Jack and Ryland raced up the road leading to Fort Hill. They weaved and leaned their bodies forward while they competitively strained their sputtering motorbikes. All of this was to top the hill and complete the last leg of the journey. Jack celebrated a first-place finish as Ryland registered a second-place finish and to his dismay, I finished a close third.

However, the beauty of the picturesque scene was worthy of Kings. It was a bright morning, and we saw the Naval Monument, Vicksburg National Cemetery, gazebo, Yazoo River and Canal, Mississippi River, and Lake Centennial. We sat atop the hill for about twenty minutes and admired the beauty that was a gift on this outstanding Monday morning.

We grabbed pigeons and on the count of three released them. They climbed high into the sky and flew in circles as they received their instinctive bearings. They flapped their wings as they glided in the morning sky. Ever so slightly they turned to the southerly direction in whence we came. We followed the same sequence of events with the second group of pigeons. We then jumped on motorbikes and attempted to beat the birds back to their coop.

We flew down Fort Hill at full speed and in a reckless fashion. I checked the morning sky for a sign of pigeons in flight. My reconnaissance mission proved unsuccessful because I didn't see any. We returned to Jack's house in record time and anticipated a victory over the pigeons. We jumped off the bikes and sped to the pigeon coop at which time we discovered that they were all in attendance!

"Incredibly" the pigeons defeated us soundly!

Final tally: BIRDS   6

BIRD-BRAINS 0

CHAPTER 20
THE BLUE ROOM

Ryland departed at 8:00 am because he had to work at his uncle's store. We were at a loss as to what to do with ourselves since we hadn't made plans for the day. Mark, Jack's older brother, suggested a cruise in his car around the Vicksburg area. His altruistic motives were evident in that he had purchased a 1958 *Chevrolet Impala.* It was a turquoise blue and white two-door, hardtop sports coupe. He was anxious as he readied for his car's unveiling. In other words, he was prepared to impress young ladies with his newly acquired purchase. To his credit, he worked as a stock boy and bagger at the Piggly Wiggly Grocery Store on Grove Street. He bought and sustained this beautiful automobile by his earnings. The car was washed and waxed daily. Mark purveyed auto magazines and enhanced his car with the latest and greatest trendy and stylish purchases. Recently, he bought a set of wheel spinners. They sparkled like diamonds because of the elbow grease that was administered by Mark.

As he backed his car out of his driveway, he announced, "Come on, and let's go." He added, "Make sure that you don't have mud on your shoes."

Jack yelled, "I'm riding shotgun."

I countered with a monotonic "back seat." However, I preferred the back seat in that Mark scrutinized with a watchful, critical eye as he strove for perfection. Also, I had the advantage of spacious leg room.

We sat upright in the car seats and resembled mounted knights on regal and heralded steeds. We felt like a million dollars as we headed on our journey.

We drove south on Cherry Street and took a right on Clay Street and headed downtown toward Washington Street. We cruised in front of the Hotel Vicksburg on the corner of Clay and Walnut Streets. Mark blew his loud and irritating horn which played a cheesy rendition of *"Dixie."* Local girls laughed as we waved back like the politicians who vied for political office. We took a left on Washington Street at the First National Bank and waved to friends who stood in front of Crowley's Pool Hall. We passed The Hub and Karl's men's clothing stores and were amazed that young people circulated at this hour of the morning. I looked back and determined that Michel's Record Shop had opened. I spent hours at a time in the record shop as I kept up and listened to the latest 45's and albums. We turned left at the department store, The Valley which was on the corner of Washington and South Streets. We drove around and sought out friends. Finally, we parked on Walnut Street and headed for breakfast at the "The Glass Kitchen."

We enjoyed a breakfast of scrambled eggs with cheese, grits, toast, and orange juice. Then, we left the restaurant filled with a spirit of adventure. As we returned to Mark's car, we noticed a cardboard advertisement poster that was attached to a light pole. The poster was from the "Blue Room" which was at 602 Clay Street. It advertised the upcoming appearance of national entertainment acts. The Blue Room was a Colored establishment in which Whites occasionally attended when someone famous appeared. There were segregation laws that frowned upon the mingling of the Races. However, the owner of the establishment cordoned off an area for White customers. Colored and Whites alike enjoyed performances by famous acts like Fats Domino, Louis Armstrong, B.B. King, and Vicksburg's own "The Red Tops."

I said to Mark, "Hey, let's drive by the Blue Room because I heard that Bobby Bland is performing this week. Maybe, he and his band arrived early for rehearsals, and we can catch a glimpse of him."

"I don't know if I feel comfortable about that," Mark said.

"I've been there a few times. Everybody there's friendly," I replied.

"I'll drive us by, but I'm going to stay in my car," Mark remarked.

"No problem. Let's go."

We noticed that the owner's pink Cadillac was in front of the Blue Room, but there wasn't anyone in front of the establishment. I jumped out of the car and looked inside the diamond-shaped door window in hopes of catching a glimpse of one of my favorite recording artists. All I saw, was an empty hallway without a person in sight. I turned around to return to the car. Suddenly, I felt that someone had tugged on the back of my shirt at the nape of my neck. I turned around and saw two White men in their twenties or thirties. The confronted me with smirks on their faces.

"Boy, what in the hell do you think that you're doing hanging around here?"

"I was trying to see if I could spot the recording star, Bobby Bland."

Out of the side of my eye, I saw Jack and Mark as they backed up the car and then sped up the hill to Washington Street.

"One of the men said, "This is no place for White boys to be hanging around. Now, go away and never come back," he said as he released my collar and pointed up the hill toward Washington Street. I defiantly looked at them and straightened my clothes.

"Have you got something to say stick man?" One of the men stated in a southern drawl.

"Yes, I do! It's a free world, and I'll come and go as I please."

"Well, if you bring your skinny ass back down here again, you'll see what you're going to get. Scram! Or get ready to get your thin, free-world ass whipped."

I turned around and climbed the hill defiantly. Luckily, at the top of the hill, Mark and Jack waited for me, and I jumped in the car, and we continued our journey.

Jack stated, "Sorry that we took off, but those men were acting angry and crazy. There were two others in their car. Good thing that you didn't get hurt. What was that all about anyway?"

"Evidently, those men didn't want me to be patronizing at the Blue Room. They could've been Klan members. If they weren't, they were rednecks for sure," I stated. "Let's not let the incident ruin our day."

"By the way, as I walked up the hill on Clay Street, I looked back at the waterfront and saw and heard motorboats running and blaring. Let's go and check it out," I suggested.

The waterfront teemed with people. There were cars, trucks, trailers, and boats with inboard and outboard motors used for fishing and skiing. Initially, we boarded the paddlewheel boat *"The Sprague."* It was docked at the Vicksburg Waterfront and had many functions. My favorite thing was that it sponsored and presented the melodrama play *"Gold in the Hills."* The citizenry of Vicksburg showcased their talents as they acted and danced. There were tons-of-talent in Vicksburg! I'd attended several performances and particularly loved the part where you threw peanuts at the villain. Also, the colorfully costumed can-can cuties high-kicked their way into the hearts

135

of many. They were gorgeous crowd pleasers! From, *The Sprague*, we investigated the waterfront from the aft of the boat and observed motorboat racers.

As we sped toward the motorboat racers in the dock area, I saw Bobby Turner who was a friend of the family. He raced mostly "B" class race boats. He put his boat in the water and asked me if I'd like to take a spin.

"Sure," I said. "Do you have an extra life preserver?"

"Sure do, grab them out of the back of my pickup and get an extra paddle why you're at it."

As I boarded the boat, I saw that Jack and Mark were impressed. I waved goodbye and told them that I'd return in ten or fifteen minutes. We vibrated, and the smell of motor oil and gasoline was intoxicating. My heart beat out of my chest, and the adrenalin pumped through my veins as blood rushed to my head. The boat jumped in and out of the water and conjured an image of the bottom spanking the water. We returned, and I stood up, and Jack and Mark laughed. They pointed at the front of my pants. As I looked down, I noticed that the front of my pants was soaked.

Jack teasingly said, "What happened? Did you wet your pants out of being scared?"

I laughed out loud at his comment. However, I realized at that moment, and with that comment, that my bedwetting problem was behind me. I felt confident that I'd never been embarrassed again about this issue. Thank goodness things worked themselves out sometimes.

For several hours, we played on the waterfront. Then, we argued about whether to dine at Johnny's Restaurant or Goldie's Barbecue for lunch. Because Jack hated barbecue, we decided that Johnny's Restaurant was the choice. Of course, we dined at the restaurant as opposed to Mark's car.

On the way to the restaurant, I saw several famous Vicksburg buildings on Washington Street. They included Blackburn Motor Company, Park Hotel, Gibson Memorial Methodist Church and the site of the Biedenharn Candy Company (the location of the first bottle of *Coca-Cola* bottled in 1894). I hadn't seen these establishments all summer in that I lived on the opposite side of town.

As we entered Johnny's restaurant, we spotted an available booth next to a few cute girls. Unfortunately, they were Mark's age and probably wouldn't consider us as potential boyfriends. However, we were brave and invited them to ride with us across the bridge to Delta, Louisiana, and to the Mississippi River sandbar. They responded that they'd first have to ask their parents. I thought that was a tactful way of refusing us without hurting our feelings.

I ordered battered French fries with Johnny's homemade sauce. I flipped through the jukebox selection at our booth. I selected D8; Dion and the Belmonts' *"The Wanderer"* and E7; Booker T. and the MG's', *"Green Onions."* I had trouble choosing my third and final selection.

"Would you help me choose a song?" I asked one of the young ladies.

She said, "Sure, what's Elvis's new release?"

"*'Good Luck Charm'* is his newest song."

137

"He's heavenly. I just love him." She exclaimed as she pushed G9, and we listened to Elvis'

After we consumed our food, the girls excused themselves and went outside and gathered around a pay phone. As one of the girls talked on the phone, the other girls hovered over her as a unified force. After about ten minutes, they approached us and told us that they couldn't go riding with us, but could visit for a while.

"Great!" We exclaimed. "By the way, I'm David, and this is Jack and Mark."

"We're Sally, Mary, and Debbie."

Mark eyed Mary, and I'd already claimed Sally for my choice and Jack's was Debbie. She was a cute girl who was shy. Jack's outgoing personality was the cure for that dilemma. Mark showed Mary his prize car, and Jack took Debbie for a stroll down Washington Street. I stayed in my booth and had a conversation with Sally. I nervously twisted my hair around my finger. Sally laughed and told me that her ex-boyfriend had the same habit. She divulged that she was visiting her cousins Debbie and Mary for the summer.

"Where is your home?"

"I'm from Beaumont, Texas."

She was a junior in high school, and her plans included attending the University of Texas to major in pharmacy. Sally was a great conversationalist and had her goals and ambitions in line. However, I had feelings of ineptness, since I didn't have plans.

"What are your future ambitions?"

"I haven't decided yet," I embarrassingly responded. I didn't want to reveal that I was in junior high school.

"It's something that you need to consider. If you don't make your own decisions now, then someone in the future will make them for you," Sally explained.

She told the truth, and I needed to start thinking about my future.

Suddenly without warning, Sally squeezed my hand and kissed me on the cheek. She said, "You take care of yourself. It was nice meeting you. You're a polite, young man."

"Thank you, Sally. It was great to meet you, too."

It was a magical moment and reconfirmed my feeling that there were still good people in this world. As they drove away, Sally waved and radiated a genuine smile.

"I'm riding shotgun," Jack yelled.

"Backseat," I replied in a deadpan manner.

Mark bragged that he had Mary's phone number and that she was impressed with his car. Jack said that he had Debbie's phone number as well.

They both looked at me and said, "So, are we batting 1000?"

"Sally lives in Texas, I countered. I got something better than a phone number, and that was a good conversation."

They laughed and said, "Shot down."

"You guys believe what you want. I'm satisfied with the outcome, and that's all that matters."

We rode down Lee Street which was down the hill from Johnny's and passed the Vicksburg Fairgrounds, Greenies football stadium, softball, baseball fields, Naval Reserve Building, Vicksburg City Swimming Pool, H.V. Cooper High School and continued north on Drummond Street. After a few miles, we took a right and proceeded east on Clay Street. After we passed Aunt Minnie's Restaurant, we turned left at the VNMP Arch and the Jewish Cemetery. We entered the Vicksburg Military National Park and spotted tourists dressed in flowered shirts, Bermuda shorts, sunglasses, and flip-flops. Children ran from monuments and cannons to climb them all before the day's end. Kodak and Brownie cameras were utilized by visitors to capture lifetime memories from this beautiful locale. The beautiful VNMP belonged to the ages, and when mortals have died and gone, this venue would remain.

Many picture albums and scrapbooks recorded these scenes and sat on coffee tables. Eventually, the photos were removed and dumped into boxes, basements, or attics for the ages. However, even though these photographs faded with time, they captured moments in time. These photos recorded for posterity a stamp that read "August of 1962." After these visitors were gone, relatives would reminisce about their loved ones and cherish how young and vibrant they appeared in these photos. Our historically beloved city was rich in history and captured the imagination and respect of travelers far and wide.

CHAPTER 21
NEVER ON MONDAY

I arrived at my house at 2:30 pm and discovered that Mitch was asleep from working the graveyard shift and that Mother planned an afternoon appointment with an insurance client in the downtown Vicksburg area. Ronnie and Mrs. Rosie were in the living room as I entered the front door.

"How is it going?" I asked. "It's good to see you on a Monday," Ms. Rosie!"

Mrs. Rosie replied, "It's good to be here. I'll be here for the next two-weeks from 8:00 am until I finish my work every day except Sunday."

She added, "By the way, you got a call from a Scoutmaster Speights who wants you to call him about a campout this weekend."

"I'm getting ready to go home and check on my daughter who has a migraine and a fever," Mrs. Rosie noted. Then, she motioned for me to follow her outside.

I followed Mrs. Rosie outside and was accompanied by Ronnie. She had an expression of concern on her face that had me perplexed. Her eyes filled with tears.

"Mrs. Rosie, what's wrong?" I asked.

"While you were gone all weekend, I was told that Mr. Mitch and Mrs. Evelyn argued the whole time."

Ronnie said, "They did, and Mitch called Mother bad names and I think that he might have hit her."

"Why do you think that?" I asked.

"I saw that Mother's arms and legs looked bruised. I asked Mother if he'd hit her, but she wouldn't tell me." Ronnie's voice shook as he continued, "I'm scared that Mitch is going to hurt Mother."

Tears rolled down his face. Mrs. Rosie embraced him and rubbed his forehead and said, "Calm down, child. God, will make everything right."

"I have to leave now children, but I'll be back in the morning at 8:00 am."

"Good-bye. I hope your daughter feels better soon," I said.

Mrs. Rosie started her car and slowly pulled out and waved goodbye. She was a unique and loving person who gave so much of herself. She always lent a helping hand, listened to our problems, and offered sage advice. Mrs. Rosie was a remarkable woman.

I felt sorry for Ronnie and returned my attention to him. He was shattered and was a nervous wreck. He deserved more than this deplorable situation. He was an intelligent and sweet kid who shouldn't have to endure this emotional nightmare.

My mission for the rest of the afternoon was that I had to avoid Mitch at all costs. Ronnie was my shadow all evening, and I tried to provide emotional support and companionship. Mother returned about 5:30 pm and prepared tuna fish sandwiches, potato chips, and milk. Mitch joined us in the dining room, and we ate in silence; you could cut the tension with a knife. Mitch sat in the silence at the head of the table and was broodingly quiet.

After we ate, Mitch moved to the living room and watched TV. We cleared the table and put the dishes in the sink. Mother washed the dishes, and I dried them. I went back to my room and read a *Boy's Life* Boy Scout magazine. Ronnie joined me in my bedroom, and we played 45's. Mother took a hot bath and relaxed after a hard day's work.

I was thankful that the night was calm and uneventful. However, we walked on eggshells and hoped for the best. Mitch planned to depart for work at 11:00 pm. Mother went to bed, and since her light was on, I assumed that she was reading. Shortly after that, Mitch walked down the hallway and entered their bedroom. He and Mother had a conversation, and I heard bumping noises. I glanced over at Ronnie and noticed that he'd fallen asleep on the floor. I wanted to avoid a confrontation with Mitch in the hallway. For that reason, I let Ronnie sleep in my bed until Mitch departed for work. I placed a pillow under Ronnie's head and covered him with a bedsheet. Suddenly, I heard three successive raps on my bedroom door. I was startled and jumped straight up in my bed and expected a confrontation.

Mitch's voice resonated from the hallway, "Check with your Mother; she has your work list."

"Yes sir," I responded.

The front door slammed, and I heard Mitch's Jeep leaving. I thought well that wasn't so bad. Maybe, things had improved and that he might change. However, my initial perception and assessment of what transpired were off the mark.

Mother opened my bedroom door and said, "We have to talk."

She realized that Ronnie was asleep and motioned for us to relocate to the dining room. Mother embraced me as we walked down the hallway and I sensed that she would tell me something dramatic and profound.

"I don't know how to sugar coat what I'm going to say to you. Well, I'm just going to say what is happening. Mitch can't forgive you for fighting him, and he wants you gone before he hurts you."

She said, "His position is any child who raised a hand against him is not going to live under his roof."

"Mother, I was just trying to get him off me. I didn't want to hit him. I was only trying to protect us." I became emotional and said, "Mother, I don't want to go. I want to stay with you and Ronnie. Please don't make me leave," I begged. "Please let me stay."

"I'm not going to deny my children over any man," Mother said. "Quit crying, David Lee," she said.

I hugged my mother for a few minutes. She rubbed my back and shoulders and reassured me that I wasn't going anywhere.

Mother stated, "However, I'm still trying to figure out the best way to handle this situation. Please, continue to stay out of Mitch's way."

"I'll stay out of his way, Mother. In fact, I was invited to a campout this weekend with the Boy Scouts. I'll be gone all day Friday and won't return until Saturday evening. Of course, that's if you allow me to go. Also, I'll finish all the work that Mitch has given me for the week."

"Please realize that this would create a volatile situation if they're not completed," Mother advised.

"I'll finish my chores for the week."

"David Lee. You're growing up so fast. I love you boys with all my heart."

"I love you too, Mother." Mother hugged me again and wiped away flowing tears.

The rest of the week, I stayed out of Mitch's line of fire. I completed my work assignments for the week. I had received physical and mental abuse all summer. However, school started soon, and this meant that I wouldn't be in contact as much with Mitch which reduced tensions and made things better for everyone. For the sake of Mother and Ronnie, I hoped and prayed that everything worked out. I wanted to continue to live with them.

CHAPTER 22
WITHOUT A PADDLE

Yes, I made it! It was Friday, and I recharged my batteries. I was prepared to camp out and leave my problems behind. I put on my Boy Scout shirt and gathered my camping gear. Then, I headed down to Billy's house. As I maneuvered down the hill with my heavy load, I noticed that Mrs. Nancy Jo was on her patio. I put my camping supplies down in their carport and entered the patio area for a chat.

"How is your precious little brother?"

"I think that he's doing just fine," I replied. "Have you heard anything different?"

"Heavens no," she remarked. "It's just that in my head, I can still hear him singing his songs." Then, she pointed at the portion of the hill where Ronnie sang.

"He doesn't know that I'm listening. I would never want to embarrass him or make him feel self-conscious," Mrs. Nancy Jo stated. "He's in his world as he opens up his heart and sings with his angelic voice. Maybe, one day we can listen together."

"I'd like that. Well, see you later, and I hope that you have a beautiful day," I said.

We departed for the Boy Scout Ranch located in eastern rural Warren County. The ranch had a scenic area with virgin forests and unusual topography. There was a crude dug-out dirt road in the nearby woods which was commonly explored by hikers. If the weather permitted a tour in an automobile was aesthetically pleasing. One observed wild animals like deer, raccoon, squirrel, and an occasional black bear on these treks. The road resembled a fairytale setting with lofty, dark, and mysterious dirt walls that attained heights of twenty feet. The roots of the trees protruded out of the walls in a twisted and snarly pattern that conjured up eerie and supernatural images. The roads were unleveled and ascended or descended in the most dramatic and irregular patterns.

Our Scoutmaster and troop leaders expected attendance of at least one-hundred campers from different Boy Scout troops in the area. The weather dictated if we camped out for the entire weekend. It was necessary that we vacated the grounds early if this occurred. The initial weather reports predicted high winds and storms for the weekend. I hoped that the weatherman's forecast was wrong.

Scouts hiked, biked, swam, canoed, and went horseback riding. These activities were at the top of my list. Some of the boy scouts tested and earned rank promotions from this camping adventure and met requirements for merit badges. My motivation at the campout was rest because of issues at home. I desired a simple and enjoyable experience.

After we unloaded our gear, we participated in an array of activities.

Billy said, "Let's go to the stables and find horses to ride."

"That's an excellent idea," I said as we raced toward the stables.

Once we arrived at the stables, we were disappointed because only two-horses remained. One was a bay with a star on its forehead. The other horse was overweight, and a gray mare that needed to be retired and put out to pasture. Billy arrived first and claimed the bay horse. I pondered over my predicament of being seen on the slowest horse in Mississippi. We put on their bridles, saddle blankets, and saddles. Billy took off like the wind and left me in a cloud of dust. First, I dug my heels into the mare's side and yelled for it to giddy-up-and-go. The horse turned around and looked at me quizzically and with wonderment. I slowly rode the grounds of the BSA Camp on the old gray mare. We received a few snickers and sarcastic remarks from the other scouts. I returned it to the stable which probably prevented a massive heatstroke or heart attack. I removed the saddle and blanket and brushed it down. I walked the mare around for fifteen or twenty minutes. Its body needed to cool down slowly. After I cleaned the stable, I fed the horse grain and oats and gave it a bucket of water. Poor old horse, even though it no longer ran, still had feelings and deserved good treatment.

Next, I checked out a pond that I spotted earlier in the day. A canoe ride appealed to me. I noticed Joe Pittman, one of the younger scouts in our troop, who sat alone on the dock. He wrote his name on the deck with a broken piece of chalk while he dangled his feet in the water.

I approached him and asked, "Do you want to row out in a canoe with me?"

He replied, "Sure, but we'll have to be careful because I can't swim."

"If you wear a life jacket, you'll be Ok," I said. "If the canoe were to turn over, then you'd just hang on and keep your head up out of the water. Also, I'll be there to help you," I explained.

I told Joe to brace himself and grasp both hands on the sides of the canoe. Then, I pushed us out toward the middle of the pond. He held the sides so tightly that his knuckles were white. He sat down with his knees on the floorboard. After a while, he relaxed his hold and enjoyed the canoe ride. We drifted toward the middle of the creek. The sun baked down on us, and I became sleepy. I dozed off and stretched out in the canoe. I removed my life preserver and folded it and used it as a pillow. The paddle was in the front of the canoe with Joe.

I was started about thirty minutes later, by the voices of two older scouts. They approached and asked Joe if they could borrow our paddles. They told him that they needed our paddle to untangle their fishing lines. He was trusting and naïve and complied and gave them our paddle. They laughed as they departed with our paddle in their possession. They victoriously waved our paddle high into the air and called us dumbass Tenderfoots.

Joe pleaded, "Please, bring the paddle back. I don't know how to swim."

The older scouts were proud that they'd successfully executed this prank. They headed to shore and informed other scouts of our dilemma. Apparently, they made us the butt of their joke.

I told Joe, "Slowly move back here and change places with me and I'll get us to shore."

Joe was scared, and he whimpered and cried. He was petrified, and his anxiety level was peaking. I positioned my body in the front of the canoe and stroked the water with my arms. In a matter of minutes, we reached the shoreline. We exited in time for the return of the older scouts and a few of their comrades.

"You Tenderfoots are dumb. That's the oldest trick in the book," One of the scouts said.

Before he said anything else, I started into my diatribe. "You should be proud of yourselves. Joe can't swim, and you left him in a dangerous situation. If they awarded merit badges for being a jerk, then you're both worthy recipients. Instead of putting us in harm's way, you should be trying to teach us skills. You scouts have earned the rank of Life and Star, and it seems that you should conduct yourselves maturely and responsibly. Also, to set the record straight, I'm not a Tenderfoot Scout, I'm a Second-Class Scout. By the way, on what page of the Boy Scout Manual is the oldest trick in the book found? I bet that you can't find it in the Boy Scouts Oath, Law, or Motto."

They were dumbfounded as I finished my tirade. The older Scouts remained silent because they knew that they'd acted irresponsibly. Also, they were probably concerned that we'd tell the Scoutmaster what they had done.

I went back and grabbed my gear and scoped out my designated camping area. Reality hit me when I unloaded and suddenly realized I forgot food. I knew that I wouldn't beg for food regardless of how hungry I became.

I pitched my tent near a running creek. Then, I walked around and socialized with other campers since it was suppertime. Campfires raged with hearty meals. My stomach growled like an angry lion. Some of the meals smelled delectable and appetizing. However, because of the pride factor, I pretended that I had eaten. One of the scouts announced that his mother had packed two cans of sardines. He asked the group if anyone wanted them. There were no takers for the sardines. In fact, they replied negatively about the stinky smell and fishy taste of sardines. I replied that I'd take them and headed back to my tent with my prize. I placed them inside for later consumption.

As I exited my tent, our scoutmaster told us that there was a storm heading our way. He made sure that we'd secured our belongings safely in our tents. Also, he checked our tent spikes and stakes for tautness. He warned us not to touch the canvas tent while it rained because this would cause a leak. Furthermore, we dug a moat around the edge which prevented the rain from dripping into our tents. Also, we dug a small ditch that led from the moat. This ditch connected to the creek and drained off excess water. We hastily worked at these tasks and shared our shovels to accomplish this endeavor.

Darkness blanketed within minutes. The nighttime filled with flickering campfires and nervous anticipation. The figures of scouts of every physical shape and size scurried around and prepared for the imminent storm. I witnessed a myriad of green army tents lined up incongruously. Most of the scouts had a tent-mate. Billy camped with his younger cousin. For this reason, I had a tent all to myself.

As I transferred all my personal belongings inside the tent and covered up everything for the impending storm, a group of fifteen or twenty scouts approached our tents.

"We're going snipe hunting!" A scout announced. "Get your flashlights and a sack."

We grabbed a flashlight and joined the group of eager snipe hunters. I enjoyed the hike in the woods under a beautiful starry night. In fact, I had doubts about stormy weather. There weren't any signs of ominous clouds or rolling dark clouds on the horizon. Maybe, the weatherman was mistaken about his forecast. I knew that sometimes storm fronts changed directions and headed to other locales.

One of the younger, gullible scouts nervously asked, "What are we looking to find? I mean, what's a snipe?"

I told him, "It is an elusive rarely seen bird."

"Have you ever seen one?" He inquired.

"Yes, I think I did. However, the snipe was so quick that all I saw was a flash of feathers," I offered.

I looked around and investigated our search-party. What a sight to behold! High energy scouts ran up and down the road and in-and-out of the woods. Their flashlights shone at every conceivable angle. Also, the boys called out for snipes and made weird and scary bird sounds. For sure, these noises scared the imaginary snipes to another state. Everyone enjoyed the snipe hunt. The camaraderie that we shared made the outing worthwhile. The night air refreshed, and we received much-needed exercise. If the severe weather held off, then we'd surely sleep like newborn babes tonight.

As we returned to our tents, we encountered a light drizzle of rain. The raindrops fell in an unnatural and sporadic rhythm. Our collective energy levels peaked as we anticipated the impending storm. It became evident that the storm imminently loomed behind the preliminary drizzle. We panicked and scurried to the security of our tents. We haphazardly ran and sloppily splattered each other as we ran through the newly formed mud puddles. We experienced the ambivalence of playful banter and the solemnity of the moment.

A group of scout leaders made tent checks and ensured that we were all safe. Also, they assessed scouts who required special attention. A few parents arrived at the camp and picked up their sons which dismayed and embarrassed them.

As the winds picked up, the scoutmaster yelled, "Good night, boys. Don' let the bed bugs bite." He added on a serious note, "If you have any problems, please report to the main hall. Hunker down, boys! Be prepared for a rainy and windy night. Things might get intense."

The torrential rain cascaded in sheets as a cold wind whipped our tents. I took off my muddy boots and wiggled inside my sleeping bag. I slept in my clothes with a flashlight nearby. In the event, I got up during the night; I had my coat and hat next to my sleeping bag. After a few minutes, my stomach reminded me that I was due a feeding. I grabbed one of the cans of sardines and removed the key and affixed it in the tab and opened its dubious contents. As I peeled back the lid, the smell of fish and funky foulness hit me. However, I continued because beggars can't be picky. I squeezed my nose, held my breath, and grabbed my first sardine. I gagged as I swallowed the first slimy, foul creature. My stomach growled and gurgled. My stomach wanted additional servings of food. However, the situation was one of mind over matter. I finished the first can of sardines and opened the second. I attacked and ravished the contents and placed the empty cans on the outside of my tent. Then, I poured water from my canteen and washed my face and hands. I drank water to wash down the sardines. I was concerned that there were remnants of food particles steadfastly embedded in my teeth. I clutched my hand over my mouth and blew into my hand and checked my breath. I almost gagged at the wretched smell that I inhaled. It wasn't a memorable moment!

The night progressed, and the weather worsened as lightning flashed and thunder reverberated all around our tents. The walls of our tents whipped so relentlessly that it seemed they'd collapse at any moment. As the weather worsened, I thought about my family. I prayed that they were safe and secure. I shivered and then slept as my wet clothes dried. The warmth of the sleeping bag reassured me with feelings of security.

I woke startlingly! There was a large animal that licked my face voraciously. Was it a black bear? I yelled and pushed back hard at the animal and got it off me. I was amazed when I discovered that it was a friendly, black dog. He steadily lapped up the sardine juice from my face. I hugged the dog and dried its wet body with my coat. I tried to get the dog to remain in my tent, but it refused. Evidently, it was hungry and sought only food and not companionship. It departed my tent after it wisely discovered that I had no food. I laughed out loud at this silly situation.

Early the next morning, I exited my tent and discovered a muddy quagmire. Most of the tents were gone. There were just a few remaining scouts who'd weathered the storm. The rain continued, but not with the same intensity as during the night. I gathered my gear and supplies, rolled up my tent, cleaned up around the campsite, and headed for the main lodge by the flagpole. I walked to this area, but it was challenging and bone-chilling. A cold front had moved in with the rain. In these miserable conditions, some hardcore scouts made the best of it. They competed to see who ran and slid the greatest distance in the mud. We watched them as they played in the mud. This activity exemplified the true scout spirit.

I met Billy and his cousin at the main lodge, and he was in a reflective mood.

"Good Morning. I see that you survived the flood last night? Are you OK?" I asked.

"Yes, I guess that I'm OK. By the way, Scoutmaster Speights canceled the campout because of the stormy weather. All parents have been contacted to pick up their children by 10:00 am," Billy replied.

"I can tell that you look disappointed. Is that the only thing bothering you?"

"No, it's not! My family is moving in a few months."

"That's something. Where are y'all moving?"

"We're moving across the street from the Old Courthouse Museum on the corner of Cherry and Jackson Street."

"Wow. In one of those large two-story antebellum homes? Your daddy must be raking in the money working for Sears and Roebuck!"

"That's in Jack's neighborhood. I'll come and visit you on a regular basis. We can still hang out and spend time together."

"You better promise that we can still do things together because I want to remain friends."

"You know that we'll always be friends. Your moving away shouldn't make a difference in us being able to do things together."

"Did your parents give you a reason that they're moving?"

"The reason that we're relocating is that we have too many children and not enough bedrooms," he laughingly said.

"That's true. You parents are planning on having thirteen children."

There was something special about our conversation in the cold and unrelenting rain. Even though Billy shared his news, I felt a warm feeling of satisfaction. We mutually shared the same hopes and dreams. He was a person who asked nothing more of me than a continued friendship.

We saw Billy's family van coming down the long and muddy camp road. We grabbed our backpacks and loaded up and returned home. We welcomed the prospects of a warm, dry home with plenty of food!

CHAPTER 23
LULL BEFORE THE STORM

It drizzled as I arrived home. Mrs. Rosie's car was in front of our house. Mother's car and Mitch's Jeep were gone. I made a mad dash to the back of my house with my camping gear. I placed it out in the storage shed and would deal with it later. Then, I wiped the mud off my shoes on the steps of the back porch. After I shook the water off my jacket, I entered the back door in a quick and deliberate motion.

"Lord of Mercy," Mrs. Rosie yelled. "You scared me! I didn't know who that was barging in the back door," she declared.

"It's me in person, but, I'm waterlogged," I replied. "Where's everybody?"

"Ronnie is in the living room watching his Popeye cartoons, Mrs. Evelyn is at Piggly Wiggly picking up a few groceries, but I don't know anything about Mr. Mitch's whereabouts," she replied.

"I'm starving. Is there anything left in the house to eat?"

"I could cook you some eggs. How many do you want?"

"I could eat three or four because I'm starving."

Mrs. Rosie laughed and said, "We only have two eggs left until your mother comes back with more groceries."

"Don't worry. Two fried eggs it is! I'll eat anything that you put in front of me."

157

I walked in the living room, and sure enough, Ronnie was completely engrossed as he watched cartoons.

"Hi Ronnie, how did things go last night?"

"Everything worked fine last night. We got good news last night from Susan. She won the Washington County Beauty Contest and will be a contestant in the Miss Mississippi Pageant here in Vicksburg."

"That's great," I replied. "Good for Susan, I bet that Mother is happy."

After I ate breakfast, I took a hot bath and brushed my teeth three times. I still smelled like sardines. After I dried my hair with a towel, I returned to the dining room area and chatted with Mrs. Rosie.

Mrs. Rosie said, "I had a dream last night that was so real that I can't get it off my mind." She continued, "And it was about you and your family."

"The dream was about my family?" I asked. "Please tell me about what you dreamed."

Mrs. Rosie continued, "Well, I was at a Revival Church meeting at Bethel AME Church on Monroe Street, and Reverend C.J. Simmons was preaching. His message was that we all need 'God's guiding hand and protection.' I was thinking about Mrs. Evelyn, you, and Ronnie as I was sitting in church and listening to the gospel of the Lord. As I went to sleep that night, I had all of you on my mind."

Mrs. Rosie's eyes grew big, and her voice was high-pitched as she recounted the story of her dream.

She said, "There was a devil wolf that was sneaking in the valley every night and threatening the sheep. There was a young shepherd with a staff who was watching over and tending the sheep. He protected and cared for all of them. The sheep were always nervous and scared for their safety because of the dangerous devil wolf. The shepherd boy prayed to God for the strength and courage to rid the herd of this threat. One night, the shepherd saw the devil wolf with a sheep in his clutches. He was about to eat it. The shepherd boy ran down from his perch on the side of the mountain and attacked the devil wolf with his staff. The devil wolf ran away and never returned to attack the herd." Mrs. Rosie solemnly continued, "In my dream, the shepherd boy checked out his flock for injuries and lovingly tended to each one. The shepherd boy kneeled and extended his arms toward heaven. He lowered his hood and beheld the heavens to offer thanks and praise to God. David Lee, you're not going to believe what I'm going to tell you next. The shepherd boy was you! That was your face!"

"What?" I asked. "What does that dream mean? How could I be the shepherd boy?"

Ms. Rosie replied, "I don't know what the dream means. All I know is that in the dream you were the shepherd boy. I woke up during the night in a cold sweat and thought about it for hours with goosebumps and shivers going up and down my arms, legs, and back. The dream was real."

"That's so strange," I said. "It must mean something."

Ronnie jumped up from the TV and looked out the picture window and said, "That's weird because the sun is shining and it's still raining."

Mrs. Rosie countered with, "That means that the devil is beating his wife."

"I've never heard that before. I didn't even know that Satan was married," Ronnie stated.

"Let's stop all this talking about the devil, or he's liable to appear," Mrs. Rosie warned.

"Let me tell you, David Lee, that this dream was about you and your family. I think that we both know who's threatening your family." She continued, "Be careful because dreams do sometimes come true."

"I'll be careful, Mrs. Rosie, and thanks for all that you do for my family. You're a lovely lady."

Mrs. Rosie finished her work at 10:00 am and readied to leave. She put a newspaper over her head and yelled back from the rain, "Y'all behave. You're both in my thoughts and prayers."

The rain fell heavily on the hood and top of her car. As she cranked her car, it backfired loudly and echoed in the neighborhood. We all nervously laughed at the noise. There was a puff of white smoke emitted from her tailpipe. We heard another loud backfire as she drove away. We smiled and waved goodbye to Mrs. Rosie from our front porch. Her *Ford* misfired again as she disappeared down the hill into the driving rain. I figured that she'd probably bought bad gasoline.

Ronnie returned to the house and watched cartoons, and I went to my bedroom. I picked up a book that I'd read before entitled the *"Grapes of Wrath"* by John Steinbeck. The book was about an Oklahoma family who faced drought conditions during the Great Depression. The soil on their farm had eroded and blown away, and they couldn't grow cash crops. Since they were indebted, the banks took over their property. They headed to California the land of "milk and honey." They faced more problems as they tried to attain work once they arrived in California. However, I liked the book because it was about a family who stuck together through hard times and adversity.

My eyes burned from a lack of quality sleep and I dozed off. I was stirred by the sound of a horn as it beeped.

Ronnie yelled, "Hurry up its Mother, and she needs help unloading the groceries."

"I'm on my way," I yelled back.

We helped Mother with the groceries, and she looked tired and spent from the inclement weather. She placed her coat on the arm of the chair and flopped onto the couch. She released a big sigh of relief because she was finally home and out of the rain.

Mother took off her shoes and rubbed her sore feet. Mother said, "I feel I'm on the verge of a nervous breakdown. I know that I'm overly dramatic, but it has been that kind of a day."

"Mother, just sit there, and we'll bring in the groceries and put them away for you," I offered. "After we finish putting the groceries away then we'll make you a pot of Folger's coffee and bring you a pack of Winston cigarettes," I added.

Ronnie retrieved Mother's Daniel Green gold bedroom house slippers and her chenille robe. Then, he brought her two fluffy pillows. We both competed and made her feel special. Mother propped her feet up on the coffee table as she placed the pillow under her feet. Ronnie positioned the other pillow behind Mother's back.

Mother announced, "You boys are awesome. What would I do without you guys?"

Ronnie replied, "Don't worry about that Mother. We'll always be a family."

Mother's red hair appeared a shade darker color than usual because she was in the storm. Also, I noticed that Mother's Aqua Net hairspray no longer held her hair in place. Also, I detected traces of her favorite Estee Lauder Youth Dew fragrance. However, her red polished fingernails and toenails appeared glossy and immaculately intact. Mother applied blushing powder on her face with the assistance of a lighted mirror and a rhinestone makeup compact. Also, she put on ruby red lipstick. Mother, drenched to the bone, rebounded and remained a classy and spiritually beautiful woman.

We turned on the TV in time and heard a local weather bulletin. The forecast called for continued rains and a tornado watch. Even though all afternoon the driving rains steadily fell the day was one in which we relaxed. We played family games of "charades" and "I spy." We even played "The Jetson's Game out of this World." We played "dominoes" and "go fishing" and "old maid" card games. Mother cooked us a vegetable stew. Also, as an extra treat, she baked chocolate-chip cookies. After our meal, we conversed and joked around for hours. Today, we shared special family moments, but things would change dramatically.

CHAPTER 24
DEVIL IN THE STORM

The sound of grinding gears and a loud muffler resonated throughout our neighborhood. We heard Mitch's Jeep as it labored up the hill in the torrential rain. We looked at each other with nervous anticipation and feared what awaited us. It was dark outside, and the rain, wind, and thunder were relentless.

I looked out the picture window and noticed that something bizarre occurred. Our mimosa tree's limbs peculiarly wavered back and forth as the wind whipped and the rain fell in buckets. Strangely, in the storm, it resembled a person who waved arms in distress. I saw the headlights of the Jeep as they turned off. Then, there was a brief silence as I saw the Jeep as it vibrated slightly. Next, a large figure of a man exited the vehicle. I caught a glimpse of this huge imposing figure as he approached our front porch. He jogged a steady gait with his jacket over his head. Empty, steel-blue eyes squinted in the rain. The wet and ruddy skin had the appearance of a three-day whisker-stubble growth. His teeth and mouth moved in a grinding manner. His persona defied nature and challenged the elements to battle.

Suddenly, the door swung open. There was a cold rush of wind, rain, and residual water that spilled into the house. Mitch stood in the doorway in a confrontational pose of contemptuousness. He glared at us with hate and disdain filled eyes. Mitch took off his jacket and threw it on the floor in front of the couch. Then, he removed his muddy boots and tossed them wildly across the living room floor. The boots knocked over the magazine rack and magazines and books scattered everywhere. Mitch stood there in stone quietness and pointed his finger at Mother. We knew that he was drunk because he swayed and was unsteady on his feet. His eyes alternated between wide to half-opened.

Mitch yelled, "You bratty bastards go to your room. Evelyn, we need to talk."

Ronnie accompanied me to my bedroom and Mother, and Mitch went to their room. All hell broke loose as they closed the bedroom door.

Mitch yelled, "I was down at the Sportsman Inn, and I heard some interesting gossip about you having an affair with some low-bred bastard from Union Bankers Insurance Company."

Mother said, "I'll take a dying oath on the lives of my children because I'm not having an affair. What man from the insurance company? Who told you this lie?"

"Never mind who told me," He screamed. "If I find out that this is true then I'll take care of you and your asshole lover."

"Are you threatening me?"

"Hell no, it's not a threat, it's a damn fact."

"There's no affair. You're listening to some drunk at the Sportsman Inn and taking that as the truth?" She said, "I don't want anybody else."

I glanced over at Ronnie and saw him as he buried his head in a pillow and cried.

"Please stop crying," I said.

"He's telling lies about Mother, and it's not fair."

"Of course, he's telling lies about Mother."

After a while, the arguing subsided, and our home was deadly quiet. I tuned in to WVIM radio station and listened to the latest weather reports. Ronnie drifted off to sleep, and I was happy that the argument had ended. I looked out my bedroom window and noticed that the rain subsided. Hours elapsed without any sign of an argument, and I was hopeful that Mitch had slept off his state of drunkenness and had come to his senses.

I slept for several hours and woke when I heard loud and intimidating thumping noises in the night. My first thought was that somebody had slammed their fists on a table. Then, there was a combination of noises that sounded like rustling fabric and strange, scratchy, vocal sounds. The noises sounded as if they emanated from the hallway. Was I dreaming? Suddenly, I heard the loud slamming of a door. The entire house shook and reverberated. I jumped to my feet and put on my pants and investigated what was happening.

I walked down the hallway and heard the distant sound of Mother's voice in distress followed by a loud death curdling scream.

"David Lee, help me! He's trying to kill me!" Mother yelled.

I ran out of the bedroom in pursuit of Mother's screams. I heard high-pitched shouts that came from our front yard. I dashed out the front door and felt the driving rain and tornado-like conditions. I saw shadowy figures of Mother and Mitch in the front yard. I jumped over the chain-link flower bed and tripped. I landed in wet grass and mud. From the ground, I saw that they were next to our welded roller-chain mailbox and in front of Mitch's Jeep.

Mitch was on top of Mother and had her pinned down with his knees on her chest. He pulled her hair as he slammed her head into the ground. Mother screamed as Mitch pulled out clumps of her hair. Then, he choked and continued to ram her head.

I ran over to him, and I yelled at the top of my voice, "Get off my mother." He acted as if I wasn't there and continued beating Mother. I picked up a branch that had fallen from the barren, old, pecan tree and charged Mitch.

I hit Mitch in the back of the head with a hard swing from the branch. Then, I wrapped my arm around his neck and put him in a chokehold. This distraction startled him, and he looked back to see what had happened. Mother fled and ran back in front of the house. He grabbed the back of my shirt and flipped me over his head. I landed hard on the muddy ground, and he gazed at me in his drunken stupor. He stood up and walked over to me and took off his belt. He took heavy breaths as the rain-drenched. He doubled his belt as he stood over me.

I looked up and said to Mitch, "Go ahead and hit me. I can't-do anything about it now, but when I grow up, I'm going to hurt you for abusing Mother. One day, I'll be a man, and you'll get what's coming to you." I stared into his eyes and prepared for a beating.

Mother yelled from the doorway, "I just called Sheriff Barnett, and he's on his way to arrest your sorry ass. By the way, there are witnesses out here." Mother cleverly announced.

Mitch looked back at Mother as the rain poured down around us. Then he noticed that neighbors with umbrellas had congregated on the edge of their yards and witnessed this occurrence.

Mitch said nothing as he staggered toward his Jeep and departed into the stormy night.

I returned and checked on Mother, who stood next to neighbors. They asked if we needed help. Mother told them that everything was alright and thanked them. I got Mother a towel and a wet washcloth. Mother shook uncontrollably and was white as a sheet. I went and got her a cigarette and a cup of coffee to calm her down.

Mother's physical appearance was shocking! Mitch had pulled out large clumps of her hair. Also, she had a busted lip, swollen left eye, and bruised jaw and body. She complained that her lower back was in pain.

"What time do you think the police will come?" I asked.

"David Lee. I didn't call the police. I was just bluffing so that he'd go away. I'm a businesswoman and need to maintain a wholesome image. We've been living a lie, but tonight the neighbors saw what happened and the news will be all over the city after they spread the gossip. We're going to have to move to another town. I'm so embarrassed by all of this. I plan on filing for a divorce from Mitch. However, I won't file assault charges."

"Don't you think that you should go to the hospital? You could have serious injuries."

"No! That would be too devastating. I'll be alright," Mother replied. She took a couple of pain pills. Once the effectiveness wore off, she took more!

I talked with Mother for hours. She emptied her soul and got things off her chest. I was a good listener because I knew that she had bottled up emotions in which she needed to vent. Thank goodness that Ronnie had slept throughout this ordeal. He was already emotionally scarred from Mitch's abuse.

We chatted until about 3:00 am, and Mother went to bed. She cuddled up next to Ronnie in his bed. I plugged in Mother's heat pad and brought her a glass of water. She took additional pain medication because she complained about physical discomfort.

Mother told me, "Thanks for everything. I love you with all my heart," She said as tears rolled down her cheek.

"I love you too, Mother." I felt sorry that my beautiful and wonderful mother had gone through a living hell. Mitch had no right to hurt her. As I told Mitch, one day, I'd make him pay for what he'd done.

Mother went to bed, but I had no intentions of going to sleep. I stayed up for a while and ensured that Mitch didn't return. I went to Mother's car and retrieved her .22-caliber pistol for protection. I locked all the doors and windows and placed kitchen knives in our backdoor door frame. I positioned the living room chair against the front door in case Mitch returned. I checked on Mother and Ronnie all night and ensured their safety. Thank God that Mitch stayed away because I could only imagine what would've happened.

After a while, the adrenaline had worn off, and things were calm. The rain subsided during this grueling and emotional night. Gloriously, I witnessed the dawn of morning as it appeared before my eyes. I thanked God once again for all our blessings. I prayed for future guidance and a better life for my family.

CHAPTER 25
SONG ON A HILL

Sunday morning was beautiful! The rain subsided, and the sun shone. The divine and magnificent blue sky defied description. I heard birds as they sang their songs of praise. They flew from place to place in search of food. Our yard hosted countless bugs, bees, and butterflies. The storms put God's creatures on hold for two days, but they made up for lost time. Insects scurried around the yard in unison. Unfortunately, our mimosa tree leaned closer to disaster. However, the tree weathered the storm and stood its ground and maintained its residence at our home address.

Mother appeared pitiful as she arose this morning. Her face was swollen and sore. Her lips were puffy with traces of dried blood on her mouth, and she had bruises on her neck, arms, and back. Her lower back was inflamed, and she experienced discomfort. A doctor's appointment was in her future. She applied substantial amounts of make-up and covered her facial injuries. She wore a wig because significant amounts of her hair were pulled out. She tended to her injuries to the best of her ability.

Admirably, she became focused and planned our next steps. She called Sarah and apprised her of what had transpired. Also, she requested her assistance in efforts to relocate to the Greenville area. Mother said that Mitch had the option to remain in the house and make house payments. However, a divorce settlement dictated a future property settlement.

We ate a light breakfast. We had a combination of cheese and cinnamon toast, with milk. Mother told Ronnie what had occurred last night. Ronnie was devastated about the situation. We waited for Sarah and Gene's call.

After they located a moving truck, then they'd assist us in moving to the Delta.

The reality of the move from Vicksburg hit me like a ton of bricks, and I was saddened and depressed. I preferred to remain but realized that we faced danger if we stayed.

Sarah returned the call after a few hours and informed us that they'd located a truck and were on their way. We gathered our clothes and a few personal items. I made sure that I had time to bid farewell to Billy and family. However, I remembered that today was Sunday. Billy and family were at Mass this morning. I remained in the house and helped Mother and Ronnie put items in boxes and suitcases. We carried our clothes to the living room and stacked them on the floor in their coat hangers.

Nobody answered when I telephoned Billy's house at 2:30 pm. I panicked and felt nervous because I didn't want to depart without telling my best friend goodbye.

I fed and watered the dogs and hoped that Mitch would continue to take care of them. However, I asked our next-door neighbor if he'd feed and water the dogs. I gave him a few cans of Alpo. He was nice and assured me that he'd feed and water them.

At 4:30 in the afternoon, Sarah and Gene arrived at our house. It took us several hours, but we loaded the truck with our personal belongings. We covered everything with a tarp and tied it down. It was in the evening hours, and we had a three-hour trip facing us. For this reason, we'd leave in the morning. Also, this gave Mother additional time to put in a change of address at the post office and work out the complexities of relocating her insurance business. The delay delighted me because it gave me time to call friends and bid them farewell.

We hadn't heard from Mitch all day. The proposition of another night with Mitch in the area rattled our nerves. However, we felt that Gene was a man who'd protect us. Mother cleaned the stove, and we ate pimento-cheese sandwiches, potato chips, and milk.

After I dined, I ran down the hill and saw Mrs. Nancy Jo on her patio. I seated myself next to her on their picnic bench.

"We're moving to Greenville in the morning, and I just came by to tell you goodbye."

"Billy is at his cousin's house, but I'll tell him that you said goodbye. By the way, did he mention to you that we're moving too?"

"Yes ma'am, he told me."

"Life is full of changes, and our lives are like a novel. There are many chapters in a book, but this chapter has ended. You and Billy can now write future chapters as you experience new things in life."

"That's a beautiful way to look at life. Everyone's life is like a novel, and we decide what's written on the pages." I noted, "We're responsible for our own choices. We determine by our actions if the novel is going to be worthy or worthless."

"I'm going to miss our conversations because they are always insightful," I stated.

"David Lee! Listen!" Mrs. Nancy Jo grabbed my arm and pointed to the hill. "It's Ronnie," she whispered.

Suddenly I heard the most beautiful voice that I'd ever heard! Ronnie sang *"Rock of Ages,"* which was followed by *"Amazing Grace."* He concluded with a beautiful rendition of *"The Lord's Prayer."* The clarity of his angelic voice had perfect pitch and was beyond comparison. He sang from deep inside his soul, and this was evident in the anguished sound in the melody. His interpretation of a song reminded me of an artist who gently stroked his brush across a canvas as he painted a masterpiece. Tears rolled down my cheeks because of the sheer magnificence of the moment. Ronnie brilliantly delivered his song on the hill. Then, I wiped away the tears and regained my composure.

I told Mrs. Nancy Jo, "Thanks for always being there, and I hope that you deliver twins this time."

She laughed and hit my arm. I waved goodbye and headed back home. I climbed the hill and met Ronnie next to the pecan tree. He was lonely and sad.

"Come here, little brother. Don't you know that I'm proud of you?"

"Why are you proud of me?"

"That's for me to know and for you to find out."

Ronnie smiled, and we sat down and had a lengthy discussion, and this was the first time that we had an in-depth conversation. I listened as he told me of all his goals and dreams. Ronnie covered the gamut of his favorite colors to his likes and dislikes of music and foods. He continued, and we discussed his favorite subjects in school. Then, Ronnie deliberated about his favorite clothes and friends. He conversed about everything under the sun. We passed the hours and expounded our views, and this was the closest heartfelt exchange that we'd ever shared.

Fortunately, the night was uneventful. Mitch probably feared arrest, and this kept him from our home. On the other hand, maybe he realized that the marriage was doomed and that it would never work. Regardless of the reason, I was happy that there was no further drama.

We departed from Vicksburg on early Monday morning with overcast skies. My heart broke with the realization that I was leaving my friends. I wondered what future calamities we'd face. Also, I was concerned that Mitch and Mother might reunite in the future. In my opinion, if allowed back into our lives it would be an unwise decision. Regardless of what happened to our family in the future, I gained strength in the knowledge that Jesus Christ our Lord and Savior was always there to protect us.

I stood on the hill in front of my house and bid farewell to Cedar Hill Cemetery. I delivered a silent prayer to my friends in Vicksburg. I revived and rekindled memories of the Vicksburg National Military Park and the Old Courthouse Museum and downtown Vicksburg. I rehashed thoughts about the beautiful antebellum mansions and all the wonderful experiences that I shared with friends. I waved goodbye to our wonderful home on 217 Ridgeway Street. Mostly, I thanked God for answering my prayers and for his infinite love. I recited Psalm 23 to comfort me and to guide me on my upcoming challenges. Also, I recalled one of my favorite and most meaningful biblical passages. The verse is from 1: Corinthians. It stated that as clearly as God saw into my heart that three things remained. These entities were faith, hope, and love and that of these the greatest of all was love.

173

Mother had a severe headache and was in pain. Sarah administered a dosage of pain medication. She gingerly positioned herself into the backseat. We comforted her and brought her a pillow and quilt. Sarah drove Mother's car, and Ronnie rode in the truck. Gene slowly pulled out of our driveway with our belongings. Sarah followed Gene, and I sat in the front passenger seat. I hid my disappointment and grief about leaving. As we departed, we passed some of my favorite sites in Vicksburg, and I experienced raw emotion. Tears rolled down my face as I picked up a pencil and pad. I inhaled a deep breath and gathered my thoughts. I dipped into the inner depths of my psyche and captured my feelings about my city, family, and friends. The words spilled onto the paper in the form of a poem. This composition was a catharsis of the soul and echoed my feelings from a song on a hill.

SONG ON A HILL

VICKSBURG HILLS
ROLLING DREAMS
STEAMER SPRAGUE
PADDLING STREAMS
PRIZE MEMORIES
VERSES SING
A SONG ON A HILL

VICKSBURG MANSIONS
LOVELY TREES
HEART PASSIONS
PRAYING KNEES
PAST SEASONS
LYRICS SING
A SONG ON A HILL

VICKSBURG STYLE
CONFEDERATE LORE
DISPERSING SEEDS
PERSISTING MORE
PRECIOUS DAYS
VOICES SING
A SONG ON A HILL

About the Author

George W. Ramphrey resided intermittently with his family in Vicksburg, Mississippi from 1960 to 1969. He presently lives in Mesquite, Texas with his wife and family.

Song On A Hill

Made in the USA
Columbia, SC
26 November 2017